Developing Lit

NON-FICTION COMPENDIUM

PHOTOCOPIABLE TEACHING RESOURCES FOR LITERACY

ages
4–7

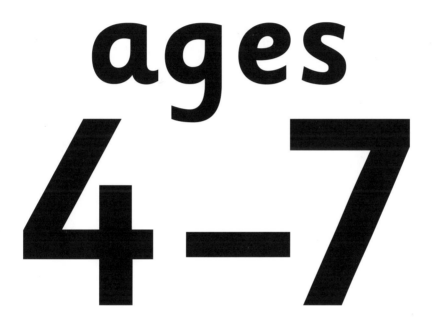

Christine Moorcroft

Series consultant Ray Barker

A & C BLACK

Contents

Ages 6–7

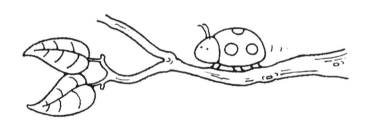

Published 2008 by A & C Black Publishers Limited
38 Soho Square, London W1D 3HB
www.acblack.com

ISBN: 978-1-4081-0054-7

Copyright text © Christine Moorcroft, 2002, 2008
Ages 4–5 and 5–6
Copyright illustrations © Michael Evans and Leon Baxter, 2002
Ages 6–7
Copyright illustrations © Gaynor Berry, 2002
Copyright cover illustration © Sean Longcroft, 2008

The author and publishers would like to thank Ray Barker, Madeleine Madden, Julia Tappin and Sarah Vickers for their advice in producing this series of books.

A CIP catalogue record for this book is available from the British Library.

Printed in Great Britain by Caligraving Ltd, Thetford, Norfolk.

This book is produced using paper that is made from wood grown in managed, sustainable forests. It is natural, renewable and recyclable. The logging and manufacturing processes conform to the environmental regulations of the country of origin.

Introduction

Developing Literacy Non-fiction Compendium: Ages 4–7 presents a collection of non-fiction activities which support the Primary Framework for Literacy.

These activities recognise that children develop their reading and writing skills across the whole curriculum, not just in literacy lessons. They also *use* these developing literacy skills to further their learning of other subjects. Reading and writing non-fiction texts, on paper and on screen (both written and audio), therefore play a vital part in children's learning.

The collection includes activities to develop reading and writing skills linked to a range of subjects and features an array of different genres of non-fiction text, written and read for different purposes: for example, to recount or read the story of an event or series of events, to give or find out information, to describe or find out what something is like, to warn or be warned, to instruct or be instructed, to explain or have something explained, to thank or be thanked, to argue or consider an argument, to discuss or consider a discussion, to persuade or be persuaded.

The activities develop the children's awareness of the characteristics of different non-fiction text types and the ways in which these match the purpose of the text. They also encourage the children to consider the structure and layout of texts and the ways in which language is adapted (tense, person, tone, level of formality, vocabulary and so on) to suit the audience, purpose and context.

Through these activities the children can develop their understanding of the structure and language of the non-fiction texts they read and develop skills in using these in their own non-fiction writing, from writing simple one-word labels and captions, building sentences, adapting sentences to suit the text, linking sentences using appropriate connectives, grouping sentences according to chronology, topic or logic to creating and shaping longer non-fiction texts for different purposes.

Information books can be enjoyed!

It might seem (and is sometimes suggested) that information texts are not meant to be read from cover to cover but to be used only for finding specific information, and that children should be taught always to use them in this way, making use of the contents page, index and glossary as required. Although these skills are essential, it is important not to give the impression that this is the *only* valuable way of reading information books; many children (and adults) read non-fiction books from cover to cover for enjoyment, because they are interested in the subject. To persuade children to read information books only to find the answers to questions could spoil their enjoyment of these books just as much as over-analysis can spoil the enjoyment of fiction.

So – do encourage the children to enjoy non-fiction, as well as fiction, for its own sake.

Teaching non-fiction

The activities in this compendium support the following teaching strategies:

- **demonstrating** or modelling the way in which an experienced reader and writer tackles a skill or approach to reading or writing, by 'thinking aloud' about what he or she is doing;

- **sharing** an activity: the teacher or other adult (as the expert) takes responsibility for the difficult parts of the activity, while the learners take responsibility for the easier parts, and the learners gradually take over some of the more difficult parts. This bridges the gap between demonstration and independent work;

- **supporting** an activity: the children undertake the activity independently, with the teacher (or other adult) monitoring and being ready to offer support when necessary. This avoids the difficulties which arise when the teacher moves from demonstration or modelling to asking the children to work independently.

Teachers are encouraged to help the children to read and write non-fiction by:

- **predicting** (suggesting what information a book (or other text) or page might provide, and how they can tell);

- **clarifying** (helping them to work out ways in which to understand new or difficult words and ideas);

- **questioning** (saying what questions the text raises and what it makes them want to find out);

- **summarising** (saying in a limited number of words what the text is about and what it tells them).

The activities in this book support different stages of the children's interactions with the text:

- **bringing to mind what they already know** about the subject (for example, by making flow-charts, diagrams and lists);

- **deciding what they want to find out** (for example, by writing questions);

- **deciding where to find the information** they need (for example, information books, electronic texts, people and websites);

- **learning the best ways in which to use the source** (from the teacher or other adult who models the use of the source);

- **developing strategies to help them to understand the text** (for example, by marking difficult words or passages, and re-phrasing or transferring information from prose to charts or from diagrams to prose);

- **recording information** (note-making strategies such as abbreviation and the use of charts and labelled diagrams or drawings);

- **evaluating the information** (for example, by evaluating the validity of the source or by comparing information on the same topic from different sources, and separating facts from opinions);

- **communicating information** (considering the audience, purpose and context of the text to be written and their effects on language, layout and other features).

Using the activity sheets

Most children will be able to carry out the activities independently. It is not expected that the children should be able to read all the instructions on the sheets, but that the teacher or another adult will read them to or with them. Children gradually become accustomed to seeing instructions, and learn their purpose long before they can read them.

Few resources are needed besides scissors, glue, word-banks and simple dictionaries and different non-fiction text types. Access to ICT resources – computers, DVD, video, digital cameras, tape-recorders – would also be useful at times.

Brief teaching notes are provided at the bottom of each page – these can be masked before photocopying. More detailed notes and suggestions for introducing, adapting and following up the activity can be found in the **Notes on the activities** preceding each age group's activity sheets.

Most of the activity sheets end with a challenge (**Now try this!**) which reinforces and extends the children's learning and provides the teacher with an opportunity for assessment. These more challenging activities might be appropriate for only a few children; it is not expected that the whole class should complete them although many will be able to do so as a shared guided activity. On some pages there is space for the children to complete the extension activities, but for others they will need a notebook or a separate sheet of paper.

Notes on the activities

The notes below expand upon those provided at the bottom of the activity pages. They give ideas and suggestions for making the most of the activity sheet, including suggestions for the whole-class introduction, the plenary session or for follow-up work using an adapted version of the sheet. To help teachers to select appropriate learning experiences for their pupils, the activities are grouped into sections, but the pages need not be presented in the order in which they appear, unless stated otherwise.

Understanding of print: reading

The activities in this section develop the children's skills in the following areas: recognising printed and handwritten words in a variety of settings; understanding that words can be written down to be read again, for a range of purposes; recognising and understanding terms used about books and print; learning how to track text in the correct direction (left to right and top to bottom); and pointing to the words they are reading and making one-to-one correspondences between written and spoken words.

Giving presents (page 11). This provides practice in recognising handwritten words in different settings: in this instance, a collection of labelled presents. It also develops skills in learning to read on sight the high-frequency words 'to' and 'from'. The activity could be linked with work in personal and social development, with the children giving 'friendship' presents to children in another class (they could wrap a piece of fruit and write a label for the present). Alternatively, bring a teddy bear to school and tell the children it is his birthday: they could wrap and label presents and make birthday cards for the teddy bear.

Sorting coats (page 12). This activity develops the children's skills in recognising words in different settings and understanding that words can be written down to be read for different purposes. It could be linked with the children's personal and social development: taking care of their own property and that of others. Ask them to read the name labels on their own belongings and discuss the purpose of these labels. Groups of children could read the name labels on clothes and match the clothes to their owners. As a further extension activity, they could make name labels for dolls' clothes.

Let's go! and **I spy** (pages 13–14). These activities develop the understanding that text is read from left to right. For further writing practice, the children

could rewrite the sentences substituting their own name for 'Anita' or 'Jack'.

Toy car (page 15). This is a simple recount of the kind the children could be helped to write in design and technology lessons. Encourage them to read the text to a partner, pointing to each word as they read it, while the partner watches. The extension activity focuses on the skill of identifying separate words.

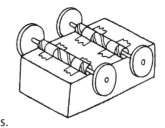

Sorting postcards (page 16). Here the children learn to recognise handwritten and printed words in different contexts. This could be linked with 'post office' role-play: set up a school postbox and organise groups of children to take turns sorting the mail for different classes. Postcards, rather than letters, are used in this activity to avoid any confusion between the two different meanings of the word 'letter'. The two meanings of 'letter' could be discussed as a class.

Come and buy! (page 17). This activity develops the children's skills in recognising words in different settings. It also involves learning to read on sight the high-frequency word 'for'. In the extension activity they might find the high-frequency words 'the' or 'of', or the words for numbers. This could also be linked with numeracy: recognising numbers and the words for numbers. The children could also look at real advertisements or promotional leaflets, signs or posters and search for any words they know.

Shopping list (page 18). This activity aims to develop the children's understanding of one of the purposes of writing: as an aid to memory. They might not be able to read all the words, but they can use the pictures as prompts and can match the words with those on the list. They could also write shopping lists to use in a class shop, for a recipe or for making a model or other item.

Understanding of print: writing

These activities help the children to distinguish between writing and drawing and to notice that writing is made up of separate words, each of which is made up of letters. From the activities the children learn to write for different purposes, such as sending messages, giving information and recounting, and they learn that writing is constant: it always 'says' the same thing. The children are encouraged to make an attempt at writing new words by applying their knowledge of grapheme/phoneme correspondences.

Balloons and **Mugs** (pages 19–20). These activities provide a familiar context in which the children can distinguish writing from pictures. You could inflate commercially produced or hand-decorated balloons and ask the children to sort them into those which have writing on them and those which do not.

Lost letters: 1, 2 and **3** (pages 21–23). These activities require the children to identify the letters which make up words. The worksheets are arranged progressively in order of difficulty and are intended to be presented in this order. As an extension activity, the children could take part in 'Word hunts' in which they have to find, in different contexts and media (such as magnetic letters fixed to a magnetic board, or letter tiles from a Scrabble set), the letters which make up these and other words, including their names. Some children might be able to find words hidden within other words: for example, 'it' in 'Mrs Smith', 'at' in 'Katrina' and 'In' or 'it' in 'Indajit'.

Get well soon (page 24). This activity provides a format on which the children can write for a purpose: to send good wishes to someone they know who is ill. You could ask the children, 'What will the person read when he (or she) receives the message?' The children answer by reading back what they have written.

Spelling robots: 1 and **2** (pages 25–26). These activities help the children to develop strategies for spelling new words by 'sounding' the phonemes separately and then writing the letters which represent those phonemes. Using the tone of voice of a robot, the teacher could say the sounds which make up a word, ask the children what the robot is trying to say and then ask them to write the letters. A model 'spelling robot' could be displayed, with a new word to be spelled each day.

Reading comprehension

The activities in this section provide opportunities for the children to read non-fiction texts, as well as encouraging them to read other non-fiction texts which they see around them at school, at home and in the wider environment. The children learn that these texts are written for a purpose, and they are encouraged to try to make sense of everyday texts by using all the available cues (pictures, sense and context as well as the shapes of words and other distinctive features) and their developing knowledge of grapheme/phoneme correspondences.

In the classroom: 1 and **2** (pages 27–28). These activities are linked with the everyday non-fiction texts to be seen in the classroom. You could ask the children to bring in containers with printed labels. Before the lesson, ask them to say what is inside the containers and how they know. The children could also read labelled containers in the classroom and sort a collection of items into the correct containers. Provide materials with which they can make their own labels for other containers.

What's the weather? (page 29). This activity provides practice in reading high-frequency words, including the days of the week. It could be linked with work in knowledge and understanding of the world (geography – describing the weather). Ask the children to write about their own observations of the weather, in the form of either a chart and symbols or sentences. They could predict the weather for the following week and then record how accurate their predictions were, using 'smiley', 'sad' or 'straight' faces.

Pond or wood? (page 30). This activity develops the children's skills in reading for information. This could be linked with work in knowledge and understanding of the world (science). The children can also read information books about animals and, with help, make a chart on which to record their habitats.

Push and pull (page 31). This activity develops the children's skills in reading for information. This could be linked with work in knowledge and understanding of the world (science). Using similar charts, the children could record the results of their investigations into pushing and pulling.

Night and day (page 32). This activity develops the children's skills in reading for information and in distinguishing between information books and stories. This could be linked with work in knowledge and understanding of the world (science).

Shops and **Which shop?** (pages 33–34). These activities could be linked with the use of a 'supermarket' role-play area in which the children can create sections for different kinds of food and write labels for the sections and the foods. To extend the activity they could sort collections of real foods (or their packets, or replica 'play' foods) into sets labelled 'bakery', 'greengrocer's', 'pet shop', 'sweetshop' and so on. For a classroom display, let the children sort pictures of goods (cut from magazines and leaflets) according to the shops or supermarket sections in which they are sold. Encourage them to label the pictures.

Writing composition

These activities encourage the children to explore writing for different purposes, such as simple recounts, captions for pictures, labels on pictures and sentences about pictures. They learn to think about what they are going to write before they begin writing and, afterwards, to check their writing for sense.

At the pond and **At the beach** (pages 35–36). These activities encourage the children to think about the sense of a text as they read it. They could also re-read their own writing (or one another's) and check it for sense. The texts can be used as models for writing simple recounts.

Lunch boxes (page 37). This activity is linked with the children's everyday experiences of non-fiction texts. Point out that a label helps to distinguish one otherwise identical object from another. Ask the children if they can spot which two lunch boxes on the activity page are exactly the same. Each group could be given a set of labelled lunch boxes belonging to other children and asked to match them to names written on cards. They could look for names of their friends (noticing the capital letters) on the class register, on displays and on labelled items such as clothing and books.

Planting seeds (page 38). The aim of this activity is to encourage the children to think about what they will write before they write it. This could be linked with work in knowledge and understanding of the world (science), creative development or design and technology. The children could write and illustrate instructions for other things they make or do in school: for example, baking, making models, carrying out an investigation or making a collage or print. This prepares them for later work on writing instructions.

Make a list (page 39). This activity can be used to support the development of the children's planning skills. Discuss with them what Jane is going to do and ask them to think of all the things she will need. Talk about the way in which a list is used: it is written to be read again later, in order to remember things or actions. Revise the format of a list: it is written from top to bottom. You could make long, narrow notepads on which the children can write other lists.

Take a seat and **Have a drink** (pages 40–41). These activities develop the children's skills in reading for information and then recording what they have found out. This could be linked with work in knowledge and understanding of the world (history): the children could observe and draw objects used in the past and then label their drawings and write sentences about the objects. Examples of suitable objects include a flat iron, a warming pan, an earthenware hot-water bottle, a washtub or a washboard.

House labels (page 42). You could link this activity with work on homes. The children first need to learn the vocabulary for parts of a house. They could use information books to find out about different houses and homes which they could draw and label. Some

children might be able to use information books to find the words for, and then label, other details in their drawings, such as 'step', 'chimney', 'garage', 'letterbox' and 'path'.

All about me (page 43). This activity supports the children in writing to give information (about themselves). You could first show them examples of forms and discuss any forms they have seen people filling in. Discuss the purpose of forms: to give information. Forms could be introduced into several types of role-play such as dentist's surgery, hospital, doctor's surgery, hotel, restaurant, bank, post office or estate agent. Provide authentic forms on which the children can write during their role-play.

Where are they going? 1 and **2** (pages 44–45). These activities provide sentences with a repeated format for the children to follow. They could be used in conjunction with a fiction text in which directional words and other words for movement are used: for example, *Cat Among the Cabbages* (Alison Bartlett, Levinson), *We're Going on a Bear Hunt* (Michael Rosen, Walker) or *We're Going on a Dragon Hunt* (Maurice Jones, Puffin). During a whole-class activity, you could perform an action and ask the children, 'Where am I going?' The children respond with a sentence: for example, 'You are going up the steps.' Alternatively, they could choose an action to perform which involves movement up, down, over or along and then make up a sentence to describe it: for example, 'I am going along the carpet.' The teacher or another adult could scribe the sentence, with the child writing as much of it as possible. Invite contributions from other children. Ask the child to re-read the sentence to check that it makes sense.

In the picture (page 46). This activity can be linked with work in any subject. Encourage the children to talk about the pictures, saying what they can see. Some children could write a short sentence, such as 'This is a ladybird', while others might be able to write a longer sentence which says where the animal is: for example, 'I can see a ladybird on a twig.' Revise the spellings of the high-frequency words 'this', 'here', 'is', 'can' and 'see'. To encourage the children to write captions, display a picture at a suitable height in the classroom along with a large sheet of blank paper. Invite the children to write captions for the picture. At the end of a day or a week the captions could be read aloud.

Learning objectives

The following chart shows how the Ages 4–5 activity sheets (pages 11–46) match the Communication, language and literacy objectives of the Early Years Foundation Stage of the Primary Framework for Literacy (* means the objective is also an Early Learning Goal; where a page number is shown in bold type, this indicates the learning objective is the main focus of the activity).

Objectives	Page numbers
Word recognition: decoding (reading) and encoding (spelling)	
* Link sounds to letters, naming and sounding the letters of the alphabet	**21**, **22**, **23**, 25, 26
* Use a pencil and hold it effectively to form recognisable letters, most of which are formed correctly	21–23
* Hear and say sounds in words in the order in which they occur	12, 37
Read simple words by sounding out and blending the phonemes all through the word from left to right	12–14, 37
Read some high frequency words	11, 13–15, **17**, 18–23, 27–36, 38, 40–42, 44, 45
* Use phonic knowledge to write simple regular words and make phonetically plausible attempts at more complex words	13, 14, 24–26, 39, 43
* Read a range of familiar and common words and simple sentences independently	11, 13–15, 17, **18**, **19**, **20**, 21–24, 27–31, **33**, **34**, 35, 36, 38, **40**, **41**, 42, 44, 45
Read texts compatible with their phonic knowledge and skills	12–18, 27–35, 38, 40, 41, 44, 45
Read and write one grapheme for each of the 44 phonemes	25, 26
Word structure and spelling	
* Use phonic knowledge to write simple regular words and make phonetically plausible attempts at more complex words	13, 14, 24, **25**, **26**, 39, 43, 46

Objectives	Page numbers
Understanding and interpreting texts	
* Know that print carries meaning and, in English, is read from left to right and top to bottom	11, 12, **13**, **14**, 15, 18, 24, 27–30, 37–39, 43
* Extend their vocabulary, exploring the meaning and sounds of new words	27–30, 35, 36, 42, 46
* Show an understanding of … how information can be found in non-fiction texts to answer questions about where, who, why and how	11, 12, 15, 16, **27**, **28**, 30–32, 40, 41
Engaging with and responding to texts	
* Show an understanding of … how information can be found in non-fiction texts to answer questions about where, who, why and how	**11**, **12**, **15**, **16**, 27, 28, 30–32, 40, 41
Creating and shaping texts	
* Attempt writing for various purposes, using features of different forms such as lists, stories and instructions	24, 29–32, 35, 36, 38, 39, 42, 43, 46
Text structure and organisation	
* Attempt writing for various purposes, using features of different forms such as lists, stories and instructions	**24**, **29**, **30**, **31**, **32**, 35, 36, **38**, **39**, 42, **43**, 46
Sentence structure and punctuation	
* Write their own names and other things such as labels and captions and begin to form simple sentences sometimes using punctuation	13, 14, 24, 25, 26, **35**, **36**, **37**, 38, 39, **42**, 43, **44**, **45**, **46**
Presentation	
*Use a pencil and hold it effectively to form recognisable letters, most of which are correctly formed	21–23

Giving presents

- **Ring** (To) **in green.**
- **Ring** (from) **in yellow.**

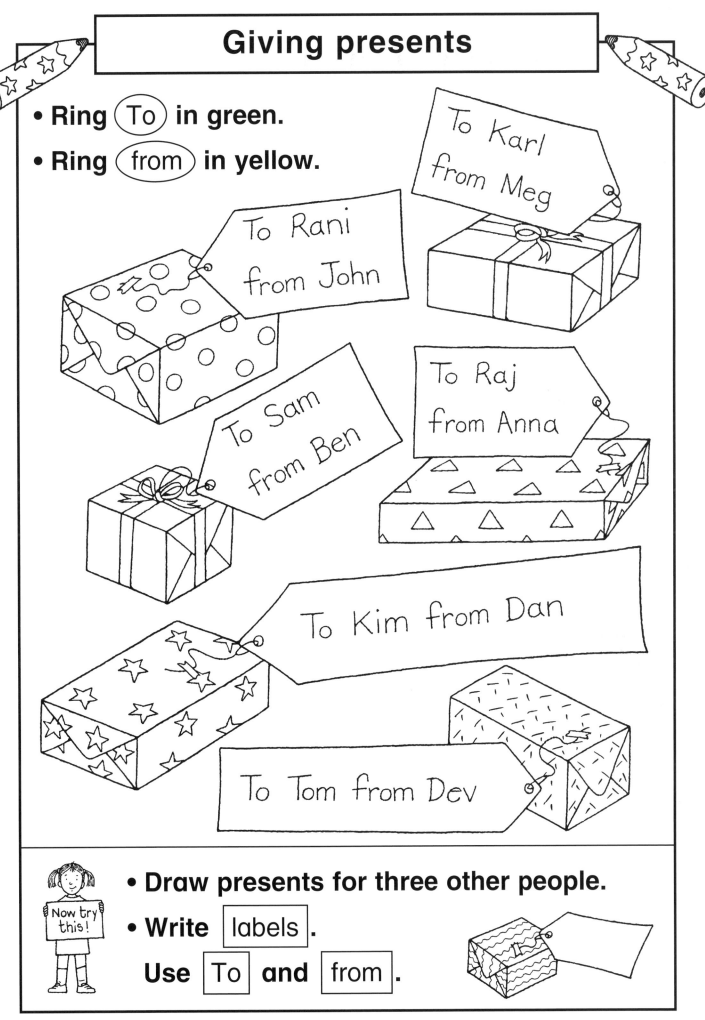

To Karl from Meg

To Rani from John

To Sam from Ben

To Raj from Anna

To Kim from Dan

To Tom from Dev

- **Draw presents for three other people.**
- **Write** labels .
  Use To **and** from .

Now try this!

Teachers' note As a shared reading activity, read enlarged handwritten labels for presents to and from different people; discuss the words which appear on all the labels ('to' and 'from') and point out the different ways in which they can be written (sometimes beginning with upper-case letters and sometimes with lower-case letters).

Developing Literacy
Non-fiction Compendium:
Ages 4–7
© A & C BLACK

Sorting coats

- **Join the children to their coats.**

Rani

Meg

Sam

Meg

Sam

Rani

Ben

Dev

Kim

Dev

Kim

Ben

Now try this!

- **Make labels for three of your friends.**

Teachers' note Before the lesson, you could copy and enlarge labels from children's belongings. Read them as shared texts and ask the children to identify their own name labels. Show them labels for the same name used for different purposes: for example, labelling on clothing, cloakroom hooks, lunch boxes or books.

Developing Literacy
Non-fiction Compendium:
Ages 4–7
© A & C BLACK

Let's go!

- **Write the missing** words **in the** sentences **.**
- **Trace the arrows.**

Anita goes to school.

Anita goes to the _____.

Anita goes to _____ _____.

Anita goes _____ _____ _____.

_____ _____ _____ _____.

Now try this!

- **Write about where you go.**
- **Draw pictures.**

Teachers' note Encourage the children to follow the arrows with a finger while they read the words. They could do the same as they read other texts. They could also have fun reading the words of the sentences in a different order: for example, 'school goes to Anita'. Ask them if the sentences mean the same when the words are read in a different order.

**Developing Literacy
Non-fiction Compendium:
Ages 4–7**
© A & C BLACK

13

I spy

- **Write the missing** words **in the** sentences .
- **Trace the arrows.**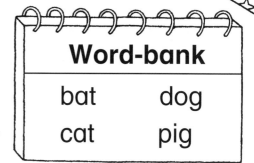

 Jack sees an elephant.

_____⟶

 Jack sees a _____.

- - - - - - - - - - - - - - - - ⟶

 Jack sees _____ _____.

- - - - - - - - - - - - - - - - ⟶

 Jack _____ ___ _____.

- - - - - - - - - - - - - - - - ⟶

 _____ _____ ___ _____.

- - - - - - - - - - - - - - - - ⟶

Now try this!

- **Write about things you see at school.**
- **Draw pictures.**

Teachers' note Encourage the children to follow the arrows with a finger while they read the words. They could do the same as they read other texts. They could also have fun reading the words of the sentences in a different order: for example, 'an elephant sees Jack'. Ask them if the sentences mean the same when the words are read in a different order.

**Developing Literacy
Non-fiction Compendium:
Ages 4–7
© A & C BLACK**

Toy car

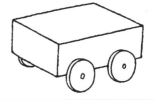

• **Read about making a toy car.**

This is how I made a car.

I took a box.

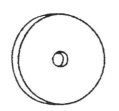

I took four wheels.

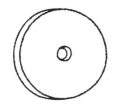 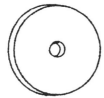

I took two straws.

I took two sticks.

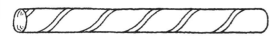 

I put the wheels on the box.

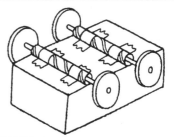

Now try this!

• **Ring each** word.

Teachers' note Encourage the children to use the pictures as cues when they attempt any words they cannot read: for example, 'straws' and 'sticks'. They could use this page as a model to help them to write a recount of an activity such as making a model or carrying out an investigation. The extension activity focuses on the identification of separate words in a text.

Developing Literacy
Non-fiction Compendium:
Ages 4–7
© A & C BLACK

Sorting postcards

• **Colour the children's postcards.**

Meg Penn — blue

Raj Vazi — green

Sam Bell — yellow

Simi Ogini — red

School post box

Meg Penn Class R

Simi Ogini Class 1

Sam Bell Class 1

Raj Vazi Class R

Raj Vazi Class R

Sam Bell Class 1

Meg Penn Class R

Simi Ogini Class 1

Now try this!

• **Write your friend's name and class on a postcard.**

Teachers' note Suggest to the children that they first colour the labels at the top of the page as a reminder. You could make some large 'postcards' to read as shared texts (they could be addressed to various people in the school). This can be linked with a class post office: ask how the children whose turn it is to sort and deliver the post will know to whom the cards and letters should go.

Developing Literacy
Non-fiction Compendium:
Ages 4–7
© A & C BLACK

Come and buy!

- **Ring** (for) **in red.**

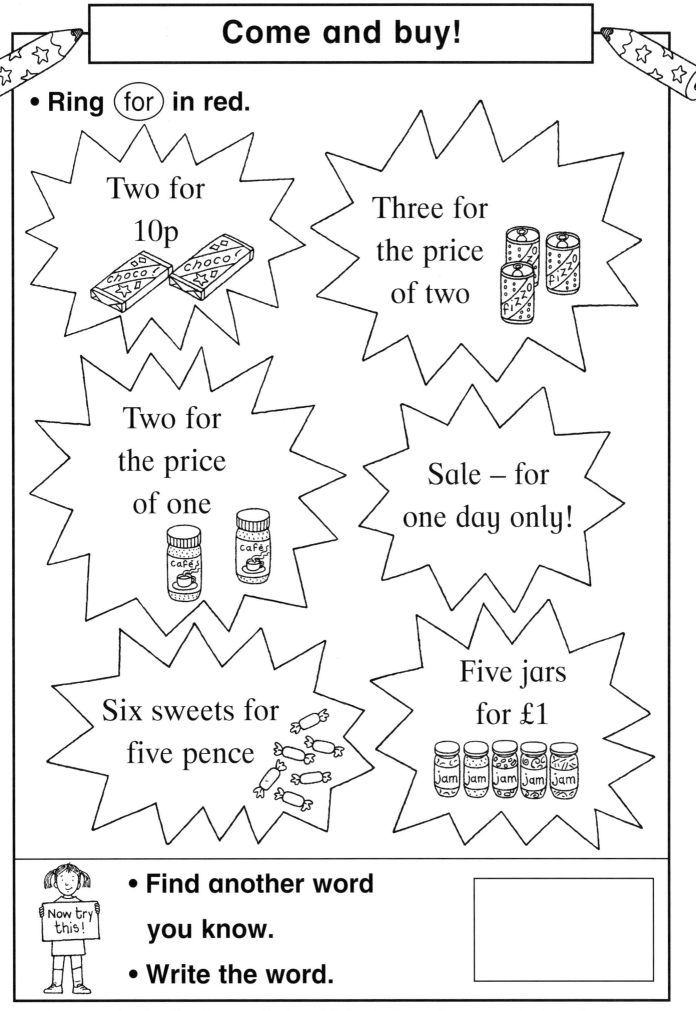

Two for
10p

Three for
the price
of two

Two for
the price
of one

Sale – for
one day only!

Six sweets for
five pence

Five jars
for £1

- **Find another word you know.**
- **Write the word.**

Now try this!

Teachers' note To introduce this activity you could collect and display advertisements (in sufficiently large text) which contain words or letters the children know. Fix a sheet of paper next to each advertisement and invite the children to copy onto it any words in the advertisement that they can read.

**Developing Literacy
Non-fiction Compendium:
Ages 4–7**
© A & C BLACK

Shopping list

Dad writes a shopping list **.**

• Read the shopping list.

bananas
bread
cakes
eggs
fish
grapes
peas
soup

• Tick the things Dad needs to buy. ✓

chicken

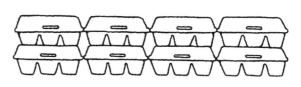 eggs

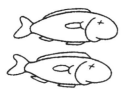 fish

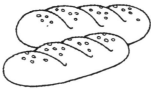 bread cakes

peas

 soup

 apples

 grapes bananas

• Write another shopping list. Draw pictures.
• Give your list to a friend to read.

Teachers' note During a whole-class activity you could set up a table with labelled items of shopping, and display a 'shopping list'. Ask the children to read the list (using the labelled shopping to help them) and invite them to tick the items as they put each one into a shopping basket. Discuss the way in which a shopping list is written – with the items one beneath the other, rather than across the page.

Developing Literacy
Non-fiction Compendium:
Ages 4–7
© A & C BLACK

Balloons

• Tick the balloons with | writing | **on them.** ✔

Good luck

Happy birthday

New baby

New home

• Draw a balloon with a | picture | **on it.**

• Draw a balloon with | writing | **on it.**

Now try this!

Teachers' note Ask the children if they can read any of the words on the balloons and discuss the occasions when people might display them. The children could design their own balloons for particular occasions and say what they are going to write on them. You could provide a word-bank of 'greetings' words.

Developing Literacy
Non-fiction Compendium:
Ages 4–7
© A & C BLACK

Mugs

- **Colour the mugs with** $\boxed{\text{writing}}$ **on them.**

tea

mum

LIVERPOOL
FOOTBALL CLUB
EST. 1892
Liverpool
F.C.

Blackpool

smile

Now try this!

- **Draw a mug with a** $\boxed{\text{pattern}}$ **on it.**
- **Draw a mug with writing on it.**

Teachers' note You could collect and display mugs, some with writing and some without. Ask the children to sort the mugs into sets: 'Writing' and 'No writing'. Help them to read the writing on the mugs.

**Developing Literacy
Non-fiction Compendium:
Ages 4–7
© A & C BLACK**

- **Read the** word **in the box.**
- **Find the** letters .
- **Trace the letters.**

Use a different colour for each word.

| on | 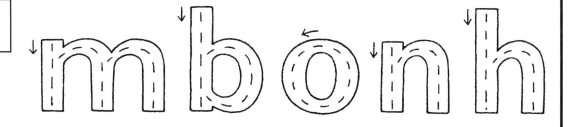 |

| at | 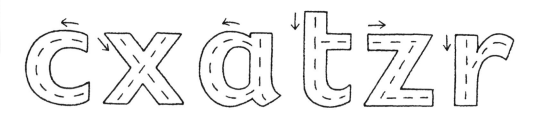 |

| is | 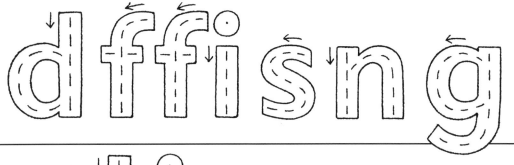 |

| up | 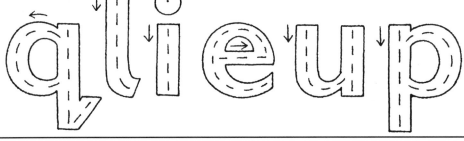 |

- **Look at the letters.** z t c o u
- **Find a word.**
- **Write the word.**

Teachers' note The children could first practise finding the letters (from sets of plastic or wooden letters) which make up these words and other short words they know. Each group could be allocated a word to find from a selection of letters. For the extension activity, explain that the letters of the word are mixed up with other letters. See also pages 22 and 23.

Developing Literacy
Non-fiction Compendium:
Ages 4–7
© A & C BLACK

- **Read the** word **in the box.**
- **Find the** letters .
- **Trace the letters.**

Use a different colour for each word.

big	o b l i h g

for	fi o n r p

the	m t h n e

you	y c o u z

- **Look at the letters.** n y o e s
- **Find two words.**
- **Write the words.**

Teachers' note You could set up a 'word corner' in which the words on this page and on pages 21 and 23 are written on a sheet of paper; provide a set of plastic letters from which the children can make up the words. Ensure that the children understand that the letters of the words are interspersed with other letters in this activity.

Developing Literacy Non-fiction Compendium: Ages 4–7 © A & C BLACK

- **Read the** word **in the box.**
- **Find the** letters **.**
- **Trace the letters.**

Use a different colour for each word.

this
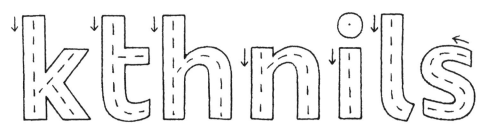

like
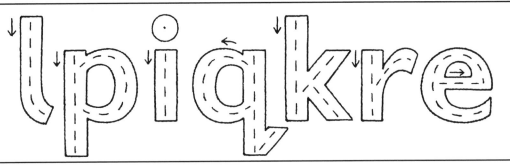

went
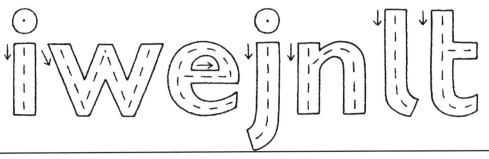

said

- **Look at the letters.** c o u m s e
- **Find two words.**
- **Write the words.**

Teachers' note The children should first complete the activities on pages 21 and 22. Ensure that the children understand that the letters of the words are interspersed with other letters.

**Developing Literacy
Non-fiction Compendium:
Ages 4–7**
© A & C BLACK

Get well soon

- **Write a** message **to someone who is not well.**

Use words from the word-bank to help you.

Word-bank

Dear
love
from

Teachers' note This activity could be introduced by reading an enlarged Get well card as a shared text. Help the children to read the front cover and the message. Discuss the purpose of a Get well card and ask the children what message they want to send to someone who is ill.

**Developing Literacy
Non-fiction Compendium:
Ages 4–7**
© A & C BLACK

- **Look at the picture.**
- **Say the** word **.**
- **Write the word.**

t a p

tap

h e n

_____

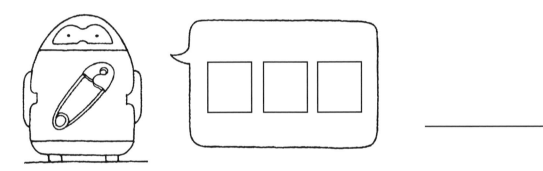

_____

_____

- **Draw spelling robots for these.**

Teachers' note You could introduce the activity by holding up a picture and asking the children what it is (begin with simple consonant-vowel-consonant words). Invite a child to be a 'spelling robot' (perhaps dressing up in a simple 'robot' suit) and to say the sounds which make up the word, while another child writes the letters or points to them on an alphabet strip. See also page 26.

Developing Literacy
Non-fiction Compendium:
Ages 4–7
© **A & C BLACK**

Spelling robots: 2

b u sh _____

d i sh _____

[ ] [ ] [ ] _____

[ ] [ ] [ ] _____

Now try this!

• **Draw spelling robots for these.**

Teachers' note The children should first complete the activity on page 25. Introduce the activity by holding up a picture and asking the children what it is (use words containing 'sh'). Invite a child to be a 'spelling robot' and to say the sounds which make up the word, while another child writes the letters or points to them on an alphabet strip. Extend the activity to include words containing other phonemes.

**Developing Literacy
Non-fiction Compendium:
Ages 4–7**
© A & C BLACK

pencils

paintbrushes

rulers

cubes

shells

scissors

beads

Teachers' note Cut out the cards on this page and on page 28. Read the words with the children and ask them to match the objects to the labelled containers. For children who can match the objects to the containers by the words alone, the pictures on page 28 could be masked before copying. Continued on page 28.

Developing Literacy
Non-fiction Compendium:
Ages 4–7
© A & C BLACK

In the classroom: 2

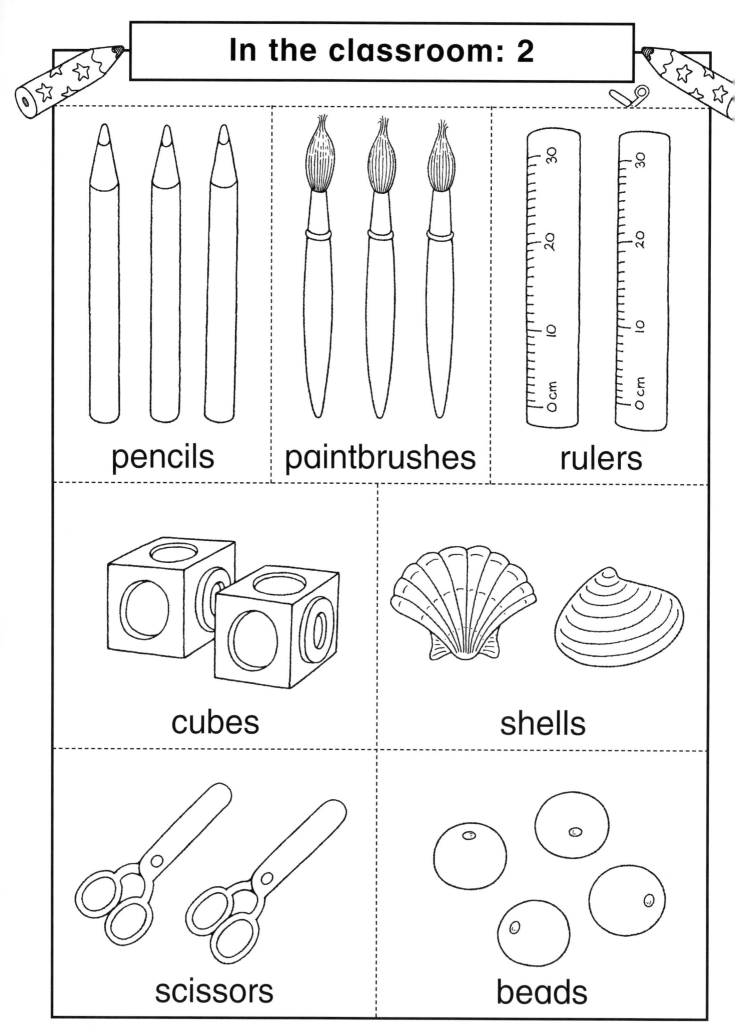

pencils

paintbrushes

rulers

cubes

shells

scissors

beads

Teachers' note Continued from page 27. As an extension activity, the children could write labels for some of the containers they use at school, or they could draw pictures of containers and write labels for them. A poster-sized, illustrated word-bank could be provided for reference.

Developing Literacy
Non-fiction Compendium:
Ages 4–7
© A & C BLACK

What's the weather?

• **Read the** chart .

Use the key to help you.

Monday	
Tuesday	
Wednesday	
Thursday	
Friday	

Key

cloudy

foggy

rainy

sunny

snowy

windy

• **Write the missing words.**

On Monday it was _____.

On Tuesday it was _____.

On Wednesday _____.

On _____ it was rainy and windy.

Now try this!

• **Write a** sentence **about
the weather on Friday.**

Look at the key.

Teachers' note A large weather display-board could be read as a shared text, with the emphasis on using cues (such as the initial phoneme, a picture or a memorised sequence such as the days of the week) to read unknown words. Introduce the term 'key' and explain what a key is for.

**Developing Literacy
Non-fiction Compendium:
Ages 4–7**
© A & C BLACK

29

Pond or wood?

- **Look at the pictures.**

- **Read the words.**

The pond

frog

duck

newt

fish

tadpole

snail

weed

The wood

squirrel

moth

oak tree

badger

acorns

- **Write where the things live.**

Write | pond | **or** | wood |.

acorn	wood		newt	
badger			oak tree	
duck			snail	
fish			squirrel	
frog			tadpole	
moth			weed	

Now try this!

- **Draw something else that lives in a pond.**

- **Write a** | label |.

Use information books.

Teachers' note This could be enlarged and read as a shared text, with the emphasis on using cues to read unknown words. The activity involves reading labels in order to gather information. The charts enable the children to record this information in a different way and allow the teacher to assess their understanding of the text.

Developing Literacy
Non-fiction Compendium:
Ages 4–7
© A & C BLACK

Push and pull

• **Look at the pictures. Read the words.**

You push a pram.

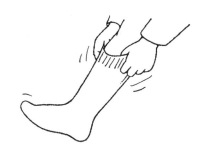

You pull up socks.

You pull a sledge.

You push a doorbell.

• **What do you do? Write** | push | **or** | pull | .

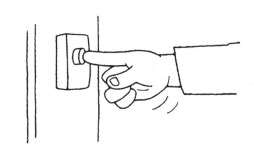

pram		push
socks		
sledge		
doorbell		

Now try this!

• **Draw something you push.**

• **Draw something you pull.**

• **Write** | labels | **for your drawings.**

Teachers' note This could be introduced as a shared or guided reading activity. It involves reading the text in order to gather information. The charts enable the children to record this information in a different way and allow the teacher to assess their understanding of the text. Some children might be able to draw and label things which can be both pushed and pulled (such as a door or a drawer).

Developing Literacy
Non-fiction Compendium:
Ages 4–7
© A & C BLACK

Night and day

- **Look at the pictures. Read the words.**

  Some animals sleep at night.
Some animals sleep in the day.

 An owl sleeps in the day.

A dog sleeps at night.

A hamster sleeps in the day.

A horse sleeps at night.

A cow sleeps at night.

- **When do they sleep? Write**  night **or** day **.**

cow		night
dog		
hamster		
horse		
owl		

- **Find out when other animals sleep.**

- **Make a** chart **to write on.**

Use information books.

Teachers' note This could be introduced by writing the two introductory sentences on a board and reading them with the children, with the emphasis on the words which are repeated in the rest of the text (animals, sleep/sleeps, night and day). If possible, read a shared text about nocturnal and diurnal animals and provide information books which the children can read.

Developing Literacy
Non-fiction Compendium:
Ages 4–7
© A & C BLACK

Shops

The bakery

buns	cakes	pies

pizzas	naan breads

The greengrocer's

tomatoes	peas	carrots

potatoes	turnips

Teachers' note Use this with page 34. Discuss the two types of shop (or the corresponding sections of a supermarket) and ask the children to name any foods they have seen there. Enlarge the page and read it with the children.

Developing Literacy
Non-fiction Compendium:
Ages 4–7
© A & C BLACK

33

The bakery

The greengrocer's

 tomatoes

 buns

 peas

 cakes

 carrots

 pies

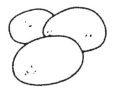 potatoes

 pizzas

 turnips

 naan breads

Teachers' note Continued from page 33. Cut out the cards. The children can glue each shop label onto a piece of paper and then glue the foods onto the correct page, using the cards on page 33 as an aid. For children who can match the foods to the shops by the words alone, the pictures on this page could be masked before copying.

Developing Literacy
**Non-fiction Compendium:
Ages 4–7**
© A & C BLACK

At the pond

- **Write the missing words.**

- **Show where the word goes.**

I ✓ to the pond. | went |

I some ducks. | |

There was frog. | |

There a fish. | |

- **Write each sentence correctly.**

They must all make sense.

I _____ ___ _____ pond.

I _____ _____ ducks.

_____ _____ ___ frog.

_____ _____ ___ fish.

Now try this!

- **Write two more sentences about the pond.**

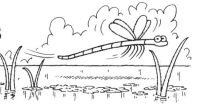

Teachers' note Enlarge the sentences and read them with the class or group. Stop after each sentence and ask the children if it makes sense. Ask if you have read it correctly and then check it with them. Discuss what the children could do to make sense of the sentences.

**Developing Literacy
Non-fiction Compendium:
Ages 4–7**
© A & C BLACK

At the beach

- **Write the missing words.**
- **Show where the word goes.**

We went to ✓ beach. | the |

There was   crab. | |

There   a shell. | |

The sea   cold. | |

- **Write each sentence correctly.**

We _____ ____ _____ beach.

_____ _____ ____ crab.

_____ _____ ____ shell.

The _____ _____ _____.

Now try this!

- **Write two more sentences about the beach.**

Teachers' note Enlarge the sentences and read them with the class or group. Stop after each sentence and ask the children if it makes sense. Ask them if you have read it correctly and then check it with them. Discuss what the children could do to make sense of the sentences.

Developing Literacy
Non-fiction Compendium:
Ages 4–7
© A & C BLACK

Lunch boxes

Developing Literacy
Non-fiction Compendium:
Ages 4–7
© A & C BLACK

• **Write the** names **on the lunch boxes.**

Anna

Max

Anna

Sita

Harry

Megan

Salim

• **Write a** label **for your own lunch box.**

Now try this!

Teachers' note This could be linked with work on capital letters for beginning names. The children might not be able to read the names, but encourage them to say each sound.

Planting seeds

- **Write the missing words.**

soil

pot

Put some soil in
a _____.

seeds

Put some _____
in the soil.

water

_____ the seeds.

window

Put the pot by
a _____.

Now try this!

- **Write what will
  happen next.**
- **Draw a picture.**

Word-bank

green	seeds
grow	shoots

Teachers' note After completing this activity, ask the children what they have learned about
planting seeds. They could be invited to explain orally to the class how to plant seeds. As an
additional activity, the instructions could be cut out and mixed up for the children to rearrange in
the correct order. See also page 39.

Developing Literacy
Non-fiction Compendium:
Ages 4–7
© A & C BLACK

38

Make a list

Jane is going to plant some seeds.

What does she need?

• Write Jane's list .

 Plan how to make a model.

• Write a list of what you need.

• Draw pictures.

Teachers' note The children should first complete the activity on page 38. They will need to have that page available for reference. The extension activity can refer to anything the children have to plan; they could be encouraged, whenever this is feasible, to make lists as part of their planning.

Developing Literacy
Non-fiction Compendium:
Ages 4–7
© A & C BLACK

- **Look at the** [pictures] .
- **Read the** [labels] .
- **Count the legs.**

back

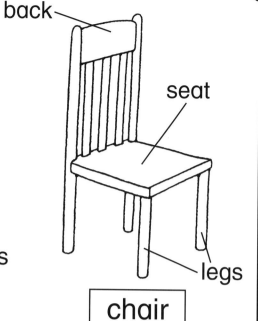

seat

seat

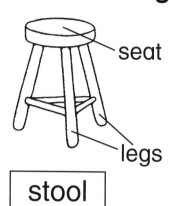

seat

legs

| stool |

seat

legs

| bench |

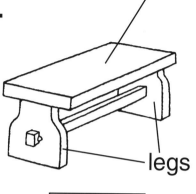

seat

legs

| chair |

- **Write the missing words.**

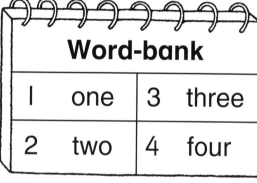

Word-bank

| 1 | one | 3 | three |
| 2 | two | 4 | four |

The stool has one *seat*.

The stool has _____ legs.

The bench has one _____.

The bench has _____ _____.

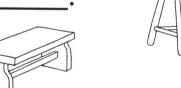

Now try this!

- **Write two sentences about the chair.**

___ ___ ___ ___ ___ .

___ ___ ___ ___ ___ .

Teachers' note Encourage the children to use cues such as pictures and initial consonants to help them to read unknown words. They could draw, label and write about other furniture (from either the school or the home), using the words from this page and others which could be provided in a word-bank.

Developing Literacy
Non-fiction Compendium:
Ages 4–7
© A & C BLACK

Have a drink

- **Look at the** pictures .
- **Read the** labels .

lid
spout
handle

teapot

handle

cup

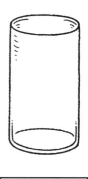

glass

- **Write the missing words.**

The teapot has a *handle* .

The teapot has ____ _____ .

The teapot _____ ___ _____ .

The cup has ____ _____ .

The cup has no _____ .

_____ cup ____ ___ _____ .

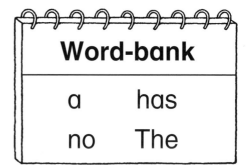

Word-bank

| a | has |
| no | The |

Now try this!

- **Write three sentences about the glass.**

____ ____ ____ ____ _____ .

____ ____ ____ ____ _____ .

____ ____ ____ ____ _____ .

Teachers' note Encourage the children to use cues such as pictures and initial consonants to help them to read unknown words. They could draw, label and write about other crockery (from either the school or the home).

**Developing Literacy
Non-fiction Compendium:
Ages 4–7
© A & C BLACK**

House labels

• **Write the words on**

the labels .

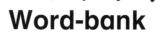

Word-bank

door   gate   wall

fence   roof   window

W

r

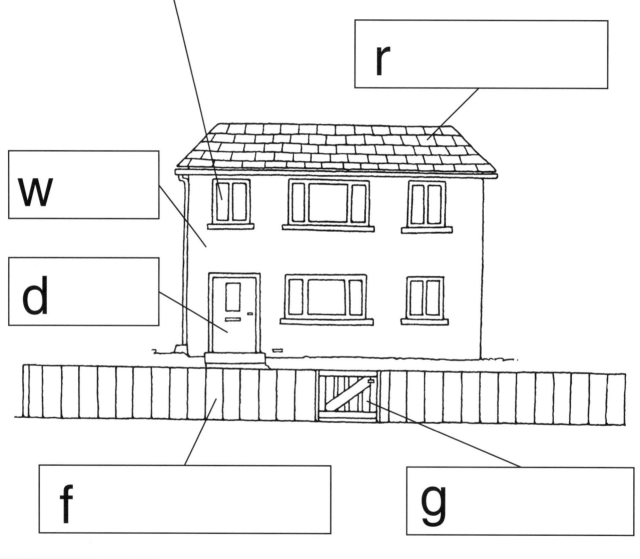

W

d

f

g

Now try this!

• **Draw your home.**

• **Write labels for your picture.**

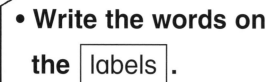

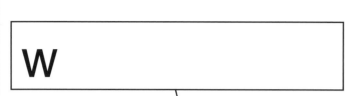

Teachers' note When reading the word-bank with the children, focus on the initial phoneme and the shape of each word. Encourage the children to say the phonemes (where they can) as they copy the words from the word-bank onto the labels.

42

Developing Literacy
**Non-fiction Compendium:
Ages 4–7**
© A & C BLACK

All about me

• **Fill in the** form .

Name _____

Age _____

Colours

Eyes _____

Hair _____

Things I like

Food _____

Drink _____

Pet _____

Toy _____

Teachers' note Encourage the children to use resources in the classroom to help them to spell words, such as words for colours and pets. The aim of the activity is to provide the children with a format which encourages them to write for a purpose, i.e. to record information about themselves. Other forms could be provided in a role-play area, such as a post office, travel agency or bank.

Developing Literacy
Non-fiction Compendium:
Ages 4–7
© A & C BLACK

43

up   down   over   along

• **Write the missing words.**

The cat goes _____

the tree.

The mouse goes _____

the wall.

The giant goes _____

the house.

Teachers' note Introduce or revise the directional words 'up', 'down', 'over' and 'along', perhaps during a physical education lesson when the children can move in response to these directions. Continued on page 45.

Developing Literacy Non-fiction Compendium: Ages 4–7 © A & C BLACK

• **Write the missing words.**

Up, down, along, over...

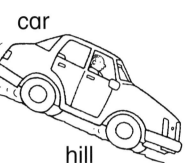

car

hill

The car _____ _____

the hill.

man

ladder

The _____ _____

_____ the ladder.

girl

path

_____ _____ _____

_____ _____ _____.

Now try this!

• **Where do you go? Write a sentence.**

• **Draw a picture.**

Teachers' note Continued from page 44. In the extension activity the children could draw and write about the actions they do in physical education, referring to the pieces of apparatus and how they travel up, down, along or over them.

Developing Literacy
Non-fiction Compendium:
Ages 4–7
© A & C BLACK

In the picture

• **Write a sentence for each picture.**

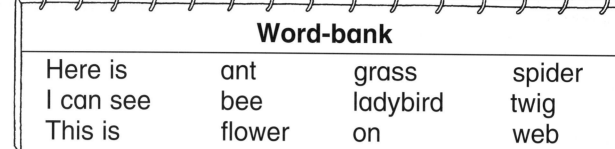

Word-bank

Here is	ant	grass	spider
I can see	bee	ladybird	twig
This is	flower	on	web

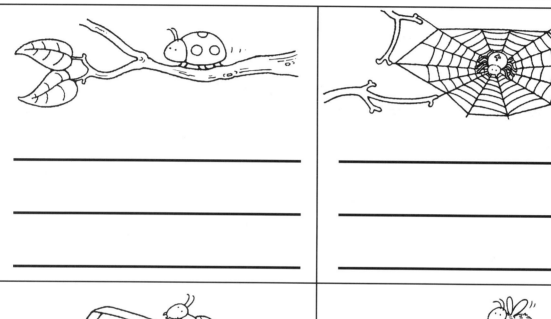

 • **Think of another animal. Draw a picture.**

• **Write a sentence for your picture.**

Teachers' note Encourage the children to find the name of each animal by saying the first sound and then looking at the word-bank for a word which begins with that sound. They could also refer to information books or picture dictionaries. The children can choose how to begin each caption (using 'Here is', 'I can see' or 'This is').

**Developing Literacy
Non-fiction Compendium:
Ages 4–7**
© A & C BLACK

Notes on the activities

The notes below expand upon those provided at the bottom of the activity pages. They give ideas and suggestions for making the most of the activity sheet, including suggestions for the whole-class introduction, the plenary session or for follow-up work using an adapted version of the sheet. The activities are grouped into units in line with the Primary Framework for Literacy, but the pages need not be presented in the order in which they appear, unless stated otherwise.

Unit 1: Labels, lists and captions

The activities in this section reinforce the children's skills in word recognition, word structure and spelling and sentence structure and develop their ability to read and use labels, captions and lists.

Hot and cold (page 52). This activity requires the children to read captions for pictures and to extract information from them. They learn to use a chart to help them to re-assemble information. From the chart the teacher can assess the children's understanding of the text. A large version of the chart could be made and used in connection with science lessons.

Who can come? (page 53). In this activity the children read a simple list of names (encourage them to sound out the phonemes in each name), and then extract information from the list. They could use a list of this type for recording the results of observations in other subjects: for example, in science, whether or not materials melt, stretch or bounce.

Picture captions (page 54). In this activity the children write simple or extended captions about pictures of places. The word-bank helps to develop vocabulary connected with geographical features. It is important to allow time at the start of the activity for discussion of the pictures, so that the children can learn the meanings of the words. They can then find them in the word-bank by considering their initial phonemes, by sounding the other phonemes (where appropriate) and by looking at the shapes and lengths of the words. This is also an opportunity to revise full stops and capital letters. In art lessons the children could make drawings of places in the local environment and then write captions for them.

A snail (page 55). This activity helps the children to rewrite in a different format the information they find from books or CD-ROMs. This process requires the children to interact with, and understand, the texts they read before they can use the information in their own writing. A large collage of a snail could be made for display, with labels written by the children. The parts of the snail which the children should label are: foot (or body), shell, tentacles, eyes and mouth.

Watch out! (page 56). This involves writing labels which warn people of danger. It develops the children's vocabulary of useful words as they learn the conventions of writing signs. It also prepares for later work on exclamation marks.

Write a list (page 57). Here the children develop skills in writing simple lists for a purpose. Opportunities for writing lists could also be set up in role-play areas such as a café, shop, post office or garden centre. As a further extension activity, the children could write lists for things that story or nursery-rhyme characters have to do or buy.

Henry's calendar and **A class calendar** (pages 58–59). These activities develop the children's understanding of the different ways in which non-fiction texts present information. They learn to model their own writing on these examples. The class calendar could become a regular writing task each week, to help the children to remember anything they need to bring to school; this could be an individual task or they could take turns to fill in a weekly calendar for the class (you could enlarge and laminate a calendar page so that it can be wiped clean each week).

Unit 2: Instructions

This section develops the children's ability to read, follow and write instructions for everyday activities.

Follow a recipe (page 60). This activity involves reading simple instructions. It could be introduced by reading a recipe as a shared text. Point out the important features of instructions: a heading which tells the reader what the instructions are for, followed by a list of equipment and materials (ask the children why these features are important for someone reading the instructions). Point out the importance of writing instructions in the correct order. The children's re-ordered recipes could be tested during a design and technology activity. An adult would have to operate the blender.

How to blow up a balloon and **Writing instructions** (pages 61–62). These activities provide a model which the children can use for writing instructions. They could cut out the instructions and rearrange them in a different order. Ask them to comment on the difference this makes.

Make a puppet (page 63). Here the children plan how to make a puppet. Expressing their intentions in words helps to develop their language skills and vocabulary.

The children could try rearranging the order of the instructions, and comment on the difference this makes.

Writing questions (page 64). This activity develops the children's skills in formulating questions before they read information texts (see also page 76). This process encourages them to use the texts to find specific information, without necessarily reading them from beginning to end. The teacher can model how to evaluate information books with regard to their usefulness for answering a specific question, demonstrating how to check the contents page and index and then how to use them to locate the information required.

Unit 3: Recounts, dictionary

These activities prepare the children for writing simple recounts (see Unit 5) by introducing them to the alphabetical structure of dictionaries and glossaries and by helping them to recognise and write words linked to specific topics.

Animal picture dictionary: 1 and **2** (pages 65–66). This activity develops the children's understanding of alphabetical order. Encourage them to use the pictures as cues to help them to read any words they do not know and to use the critical features of the words, such as letter combinations they know (for example 'oa' and 'ow'). You could cut out the pictures and captions, and mix them up for the children to rearrange in alphabetical order. You could also separate the labels from the pictures and ask the children to match them.

A dictionary (page 67). Before they begin, the children need to know the names of the shapes which are shown. This could be linked with work in numeracy, in which they will have learned all but 'oval'. Revise the other shapes and introduce 'oval'. Model the approach to spelling difficult words: for example, 'square': 'It begins with 's'.' (Ask the children which letter represents the phoneme 's'.) 'Then there's a 'qu' sound…' (Ask the children how they could write that sound and if, as is likely, they suggest 'k' then 'w', write these letters.) Continue to the end of the word, which is likely to be spelled wrongly (for example, 'skwer'). Ask the children if it looks right. Some of them might remember, having seen 'square' in mathematics books, that it contains 'q'; they might even remember how to spell it. Show them how to use their knowledge of the first letter of a word to find it in a picture dictionary.

A glossary (page 68). This activity develops the children's ability to use alphabetically organised lists and to understand the purpose of a glossary. It also helps them to develop strategies for independent reading, including how to approach new words and how to understand a text. You could introduce the activity through an appropriate shared text, modelling the use of a glossary to find the meanings of difficult words.

Topic words: 1 and **2** (pages 69–70). These pages help the children to read new words, using pictures as cues. They also learn to recognise words linked with specific topics and organise them into 'topic' sets. The children can repeat the game, choosing a new topic and using the second record card.

Unit 4: Information texts

These activities develop the children's ability to distinguish between fiction and non-fiction texts and help them to recognise the important features of information texts.

Fiction or non-fiction? (page 71). This helps the children to distinguish between fiction and non-fiction books. Introduce the terms 'fiction' and 'non-fiction' and invite different children to choose a fiction book or a non-fiction book from a collection. Ask them how they can tell what kind of book it is, and point out the distinctive features of non-fiction books: the kind of title and front cover illustration, the back cover blurb, the contents page, the glossary and index and the layout of pages (including features such as labelled diagrams and charts).

Front cover (page 72). This activity focuses on the vocabulary associated with books. Hold up a big book version of a non-fiction book and revise the words 'author', 'picture' (and 'illustration') and 'title'. Ask different children to come out and point to these features. Introduce the word 'series'. Show the children several books which belong to a series, and point out the title of each book and the series title.

Parts of a page: 1 and **2** (pages 73–74). This activity can be used to introduce or revise vocabulary connected with books (text, illustration, heading, diagram, caption and so on). It helps the children to understand the features and structure of a non-chronological report. They could look for these features in other information books.

Which book? and **Finding out** (pages 75–76). These activities introduce the idea of using information books for a purpose: to find out something specific. During the introductory session, you could model this approach: for example, tell the children that you want to find out about wood, so you have chosen 'these books' (show the children about three or four suitable books). Read out the titles of the books and point out what else made you think these books might help (for example, the contents page, index or glossary). You could include books on materials and forests. Talk about what can be found out about wood from the books. You could also include a book which will not be of any use: ask the children to identify the book which will not help you.

A fly and a spider (page 77). This activity develops the children's skills in reading for information, by finding information from labelled diagrams. It could be introduced through a shared text in which there are labelled diagrams: ask the children questions which they can answer from the diagrams. This is also an opportunity to revise the features of sentences.

Where is it? (page 78). This activity helps the children to use labelled drawings as sources of information. You could display large coloured pictures and encourage the children to write questions about them for others to write the answers. Display the questions and answers alongside the pictures and encourage the children to talk about them during discussion times.

A hundred years ago (page 79). Here the children write a simple non-chronological report using information from labelled pictures. Work in history could be based on the discussion of pictures showing how people carried out household tasks such as cooking and cleaning 100 years ago. In literacy lessons, the children could then write non-chronological reports about the pictures.

Making charts (page 80). This activity provides a structure to help the children to organise the information they find in information books. They could draw similar charts for collecting information on other topics. Discuss the ways in which the chart can be adapted for the extension activity (for instance, if the children find foods which come from neither plants nor animals, such as water or salt).

Village report (page 81). This focuses on writing a non-chronological report. The children could first read a non-chronological report about a picture, but with some of the words masked; they supply the missing words. This technique could also be used in shared and guided reading: encourage the children to think about the meaning of what they are reading by asking them to predict masked words.

Plan a non-fiction book: 1 and **2** (pages 82–83). These pages develop the children's understanding of the features and language of non-fiction texts (see also pages 68, 71, 72, 73, 74, 75 and 76). Using a published non-fiction text, discuss the purpose of the cover, title page, contents page and index and ask the children to identify these features in other books. As an additional extension activity, the children could read

through the text of their book with a partner and make a note of any words they think should be in the index, and on which pages they appear. They could then put the words in alphabetical order with the help of a ready-prepared alphabet grid (most children will be able to order the words by first letter only, but some might be able to take into account the second letter).

Unit 5: Recount (fact and fiction)

In this section, the children consolidate their ability to distinguish between fiction and non-fiction. They learn to recognise the features of simple recounts (time connectives, past tense, chronological order, etc.) and use them in their own writing.

On the beach (page 84). This is a simple recount of the kind which the children will meet in illustrated information books. Invite four children to come out to the front of the class, to choose something they can see through the window and to say, 'I saw a …' Write their names and the things they saw on a diagram like the one on this page; with the class, read the names and words, and invite them to draw lines to link the children's names with the things they saw.

That's not right! (page 85). This activity introduces simple chronological recounts. Before beginning the activity, you could read out 'mixed-up recounts' which you have prepared: for example, 'I washed the breakfast dishes. I ate my breakfast. I made some toast.' Ask the children what the correct order should be. During the plenary session, the children could make up and enact their own 'mixed-up recounts'. Provide a word-bank to help them.

What happened next? (page 86). This activity focuses on the connective words used in recounts. To introduce it you could write the words 'first', 'next', 'then' and 'when' on the board and read them with the class. You could also read a non-fiction recount as a shared text, with the connective words masked, and ask the children to supply the missing words.

What did you do? (page 87). This activity is a development of the activity on page 86. It provides support for the writing of a simple chronological recount. It encourages the children to plan their writing and to relate the events in the order in which they happened, using words related to time. Ask the children to read what they have written and to decide if it is in the correct order; if not, they could cut out the boxes, re-order them and glue them into a notebook. When writing any recount, the children could use this process, which enables them to re-organise their work without having to re-write it. Using a word-processor they could learn to highlight and move pieces of text until they are happy with the result.

Learning objectives

The following chart shows how the Ages 5–6 activity sheets (pages 52–87) match the learning objectives addressed by the Year 1 units in the Non-fiction block of the Primary Framework for Literacy. (Where a page number is shown in bold type, this indicates the learning objective is the main focus of the activity.)

Objectives	Unit 1: Labels, lists and captions	Unit 2: Instructions	Unit 3: Recounts, dictionary	Unit 4: Information texts	Unit 5: Recount (fact and fiction)
Group discussion and interaction					
Ask and answer questions, make relevant contributions, offer suggestions and take turns			69		
Word recognition: decoding (reading) and encoding (spelling)					
Recognise automatically an increasing number of familiar high frequency words	52–54, 56, 58, 59	60, 63, 64	65, 66, **69**, **70**	71–75, 77–81	84, 85, 86
Read more challenging texts which can be decoded using their acquired phonic knowledge and skills, along with automatic recognition of high frequency words	54	60			84
Read and spell phonically decodable two- and three-syllable words	54, 56–59	60–63	**65**, **66**, 67–70	71, 72, 77–81	84
Word structure and spelling					
Spell new words using phonics as the prime approach	57		**67**		
Read and spell phonically decodable two- and three-syllable words	54, 56–59	60–63	65–70	71, 72, 77–81	84
Understanding and interpreting texts					
Find specific information in simple texts	**52**, **53**, 55, **58**, **59**		67, 68	**76**, 77, 78	**84**
Recognise the main elements that shape different texts	57	60–63	67, **68**	71, 72, **73**, **74**, 77, 80–83	

Objectives	Unit 1: Labels, lists and captions	Unit 2: Instructions	Unit 3: Recounts, dictionary	Unit 4: Information texts	Unit 5: Recount (fact and fiction)
Engaging with and responding to texts					
Select books for personal reading and give reasons for choices				**75**, 76	
Distinguish fiction and non-fiction texts and the different purposes for reading them	53, 55	60–64	67, 68	**71**, **72**, 73–81	84
Creating and shaping texts					
Independently choose what to write about, plan and follow it through				82	87
Convey information and ideas in simple non-narrative forms	54, 55, **56**, 57–59			72, 75, 80, 82, 83	84
Find and use new and interesting words and phrases, including 'story language'			69, 70		
Create short simple texts on paper and on screen which combine words with images (and sounds)	54–57	63, 64		**77**, 82, 83	87
Text structure and organisation					
Write chronological and non-chronological texts using simple structures	54, **55**, **57**	60, **61**, 62, 63	69	77, **79**, **80**, **81**, 82, 83	**85**, **87**
Group written sentences together in chunks of meaning or subject		**60**, 61, 62		77, **82**, **83**	85, 87
Sentence structure and punctuation					
Compose and write simple sentences independently to communicate meaning	**54**, 58, 59	61, **62**, **63**, **64**		76, 77, **78**, 79	85, **86**, 87
Use capital letters and full stops when punctuating simple sentences	54, 58, 59	62–64		76–78	87

Hot and cold

- **Read the** captions .
- **Write on the** chart . hot cold

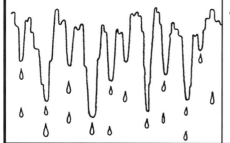		
Ice is cold.	A kettle is hot.	The sun is hot.

Snow is cold.	A fire is hot.	A fridge is cold.

Cold things	Hot things
ice	

- **Write two other** cold **things on the chart.**
- **Write two other** hot **things on the chart.**

Teachers' note Encourage the children to use the pictures as cues to help them to read the text. They should learn to spell 'hot' and 'cold' by sounding the phonemes.

**Developing Literacy
Non-fiction Compendium:
Ages 4–7**
© A & C BLACK

Who can come?

- **Read the party** `list` **.**

  These children can come: `✔`

  These children cannot come: `✗`

- **Write** `yes` **or** `no` **.**

Party list

Adam	✔
Ben	✔
Gita	✔
Jack	✗
Kelly	✗
Lisa	✔
Meg	✔
Sam	✗

Can Gita come?

`yes`

Can Lisa come?

Can Jack come?

Can Adam come?

Can Sam come?

Can Meg come?

- **Who else can come to the party?**

- **Who else cannot come?**

Now try this!

Write sentences.

Teachers' note Point out the features of this type of list: the names are written one below the other. After the children have completed the activity, provide them with long sheets of paper on which to list the members of their group (one below the other). They can use the list as a checklist for everyday school activities (for example, to answer the question, 'Who is having school lunch?').

Developing Literacy
Non-fiction Compendium:
Ages 4–7
© A & C BLACK

Picture captions

- **Write a** `caption` **for each picture.**

Word-bank

lake	countryside	postbox	grass
swings	mountains	park	river
litter bin	pond	clouds	wood

The street has a fish and chips shop, a

_____

_____

_____

- **Draw a picture of a place you know.**
- **Write a caption.**

Teachers' note To introduce the activity, show the class an enlarged copy of the page. Discuss what the children can see in each picture and ask them what kind of place each picture shows. Invite them to give a sentence about each picture. Some children could write simple captions (for example, 'This is a street'), while others might be able to write extended captions.

Developing Literacy
Non-fiction Compendium:
Ages 4–7
© A & C BLACK

- **Find out about the parts of a snail.**
- **Write the** labels **.**

Use non-fiction texts.

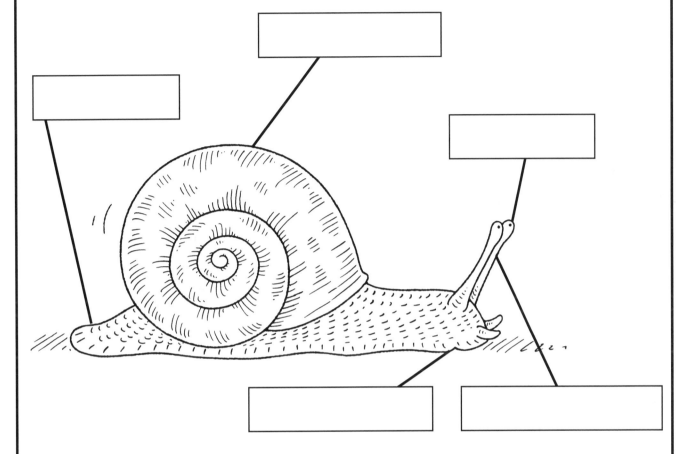

- **Write three** sentences **about a snail.**

_____

_____

_____

Now try this!

- **Find out about a worm.**
- **Draw a picture of a worm.**
- **Label your picture.**
- **Write a sentence about a worm.**

Use non-fiction texts.

Teachers' note At the start of the activity, ask the children if they know the names of any of the parts of a snail which have lines pointing to them. Model how to check their ideas using information books.

Developing Literacy
Non-fiction Compendium:
Ages 4–7
© A & C BLACK

Watch out!

• **Write the words on the warning** signs .

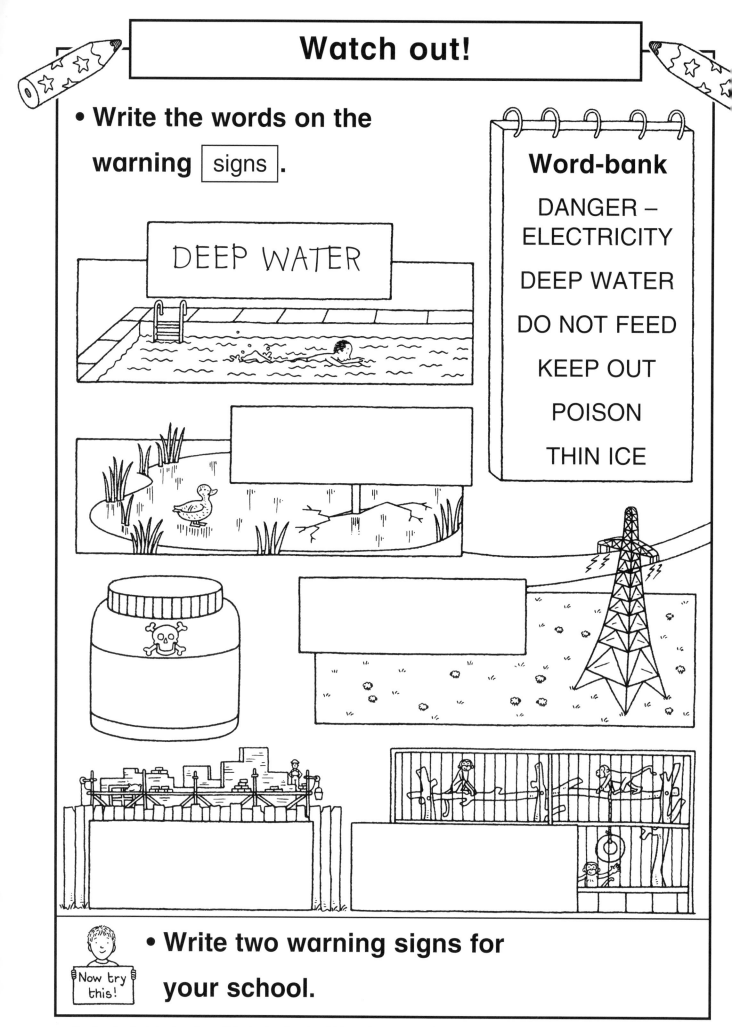

DEEP WATER

Word-bank

DANGER – ELECTRICITY

DEEP WATER

DO NOT FEED

KEEP OUT

POISON

THIN ICE

• **Write two warning signs for your school.**

Now try this!

Teachers' note Introduce the activity by showing the children pictures, or real examples, of warning signs (for example, signs around the school and in the neighbourhood, and warnings on containers). Read the signs with the children and discuss why the signs are used. Point out that warning signs are usually written in capital letters and do not need to be in sentences; they can be one or two words.

Developing Literacy
Non-fiction Compendium:
Ages 4–7
© A & C BLACK

Write a list

- **Write Carl's** list **of things to do.**

 Use a dictionary.

Carl's list of things to do

read his book

 Now try this!

- **Write a list of things you have to do today.**

Teachers' note Introduce the activity by reading an enlarged copy of a list, such as a shopping list or aide-memoire, which has been used in real life (with the items ticked to show which things have been bought or carried out). Talk about why people make such lists and how they use them. Discuss whether lists need to be written in any particular order.

Developing Literacy Non-fiction Compendium: Ages 4–7
© A & C BLACK

Henry's calendar

- **Read Henry's** calendar .

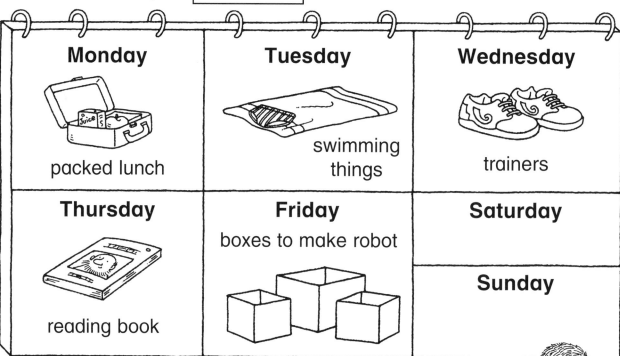

What will Henry bring to school?

- **Fill in the gaps.**

1. On Monday Henry will bring a _____

_____

2. On Tuesday Henry will bring his _____

_____

3. On Wednesday Henry will _____

_____

4. On Thursday Henry _____

_____

5. On Friday _____

_____

Teachers' note Revise the days of the week. Read the calendar with the children and explain that it shows what Henry has to remember to bring to school this week. Discuss why Saturday and Sunday are left blank. As an extension, some children could work out, from the calendar, what Henry will be doing at school each day, and write sentences about this.

Developing Literacy
Non-fiction Compendium:
Ages 4–7
© A & C BLACK

A class calendar

What do the children do at school each day?

• **Look at the** calendar .

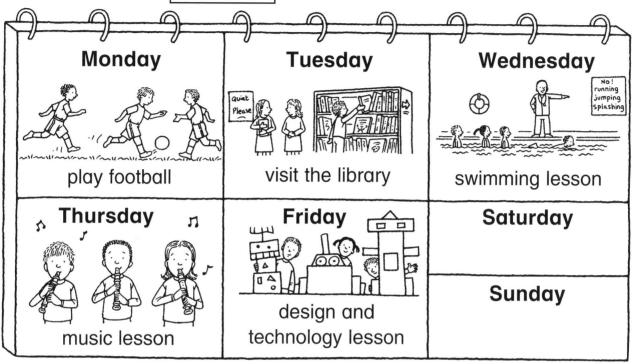

Monday — play football
Tuesday — visit the library
Wednesday — swimming lesson
Thursday — music lesson
Friday — design and technology lesson
Saturday
Sunday

• **Fill in the gaps.**

1. On Monday the children _____

2. On Tuesday the _____

3. On Wednesday _____

_____

4. On _____

_____

5. On _____

_____

Now try this!

• **Fill in a calendar for your week at school.**

Write and draw.

Teachers' note The children should first complete the activity on page 58. For the extension activity, create a word-bank by talking about what the children will be doing at school each day, and what they need to bring. Give them an enlarged calendar page to fill in, or a simple calendar template like the one on this page.

**Developing Literacy
Non-fiction Compendium:
Ages 4–7
© A & C BLACK**

Follow a recipe

- **Cut out the pictures.**
- **Put them in order.**

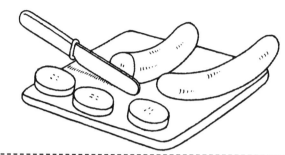

- **Cut out the** instructions **.**
- **Put the correct one below each picture.**
- **Glue the pictures and words onto paper.**

Now try this!

Slice the bananas.

Banana drink

You need:
2 bananas
250 ml milk
1 carton yogurt
blender
knife
chopping board

Pour the mixture into four glasses.

Mix the sliced bananas, milk and yogurt in a blender.

Teachers' note The children work in groups of four. They need a large sheet of paper onto which they can glue the cut-out cards. During a follow-up lesson provide the equipment and materials for making the drink and invite one group to follow a set of instructions which another group has assembled. Ensure that a blunt knife is used and an adult operates the blender.

Developing Literacy
Non-fiction Compendium:
Ages 4–7
© A & C BLACK

How to blow up a balloon

- **Look at the pictures.**
- **Complete the** | instructions | **for blowing up a balloon.**

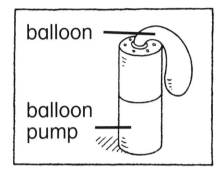

balloon

balloon
pump

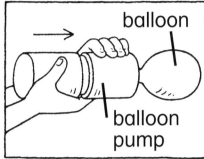

balloon

balloon
pump

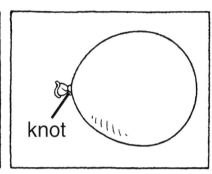

knot

You need:

_____
_____
_____

1. Put the balloon _____

_____

2. Push _____

_____

3. When the balloon _____

_____

_____

Now try this!

- **Write a warning sign about blowing up balloons.**

Teachers' note Demonstrate blowing up a balloon (using a balloon pump) and ask the children to say what you are doing at each stage. Warn the children that they should never attempt to blow up a balloon with their mouth (see extension activity). Talk about the layout of the instructions and the order in which they should be written.

**Developing Literacy
Non-fiction Compendium:
Ages 4–7
© A & C BLACK**

Writing instructions

How to _____

_____

What do you know about?

You need:

_____

_____

_____

_____

1.

2.

3.

Teachers' note The children should first complete the activity on page 61. Use this page as a framework to help them to write instructions for something they know how to do. Model the structure: 'First I …, Then I …, Next I …'. (See also pages 85 and 86 for activities practising ordering sentences and using time connectives.)

Developing Literacy
Non-fiction Compendium:
Ages 4–7
© A & C BLACK

Make a puppet

Emma is going to make a puppet.

- **Write** **instructions** **to tell her what to do.**

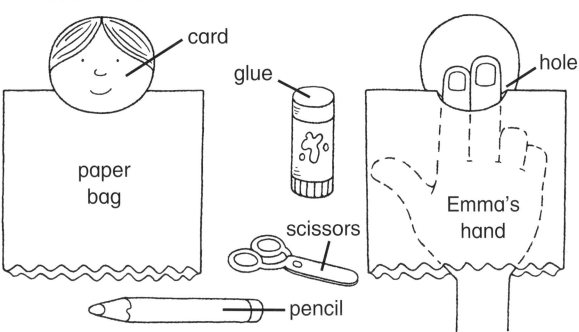

Front view

card

paper bag

Back view

glue

hole

Emma's hand

scissors

pencil

Make a paper bag puppet

You need a paper bag, some card, scissors, _____ and a _____ .

1. Cut a hole in _____

2. Draw a face on _____

3. Glue the face _____

4. Put your hand _____

Now try this!

- **Follow your instructions. Do they work?**

Teachers' note Ask the children what Emma has to do before she begins to make the puppet, i.e. collect the materials and equipment. You could show them a ready-made puppet like the one illustrated, and model the planning process, but without having the materials to hand: for example, say, 'I'm going to cut a hole in a paper bag – what must I do first?'

Developing Literacy
Non-fiction Compendium:
Ages 4–7
© A & C BLACK

- **Look at this game.**

Word-bank

ball
goal
mouth
play
score
tube

how
what
when
why

What do you want to know about the game?

- **Write some** [questions] .

What _____

_____

_____

_____

_____

_____

Now try this!

- **Write an answer to one of your questions.**

Ask older people.

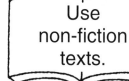

Use non-fiction texts.

Teachers' note Explain that the picture shows an old game. Ask what the children on the box are doing. What clues are there in the picture and in the words? Record the children's responses and then re-read them. Ask them what they do not know about the game. For the extension, provide suitable information books (the children could also ask older people in the school).

Developing Literacy
Non-fiction Compendium:
Ages 4–7
© A & C BLACK

- **Write the first** | letter | .
- **Read the** | word | .

 _a_ nt	 ___ utterfly	 ___ ow
 ___ og	 ___ lephant	 ___ ish
 ___ oat	 ___ orse	 ___ guana
 ___ ellyfish	 ___ angaroo	 ___ ion

Teachers' note Use this with page 66. You could revise alphabetical order by playing 'alphabetical shopping'. Begin 'Today I went shopping and I bought an apple. Today I went shopping and I bought a banana…' Invite the children to continue. Point out the importance of sentences making sense.

Developing Literacy
Non-fiction Compendium:
Ages 4–7
© A & C BLACK

Animal picture dictionary: 2

- **Write the first** [letter] .
- **Read the** [word] .

It is hard to find animals for [q] , [u] and [x] .

Can you find any?

___ ouse

___ ewt

___ ctopus

___ ig

___ abbit

___ eal

___ iger

___ ulture

___ alrus

___ ak

___ ebra

Teachers' note Use this with page 65. When the children have completed the activity sheets, draw their attention to the first letters of the words and ask what they notice. Ask them which letters of the alphabet are missing, and why.

Developing Literacy
Non-fiction Compendium:
Ages 4–7
© A & C BLACK

A dictionary

- **Complete the** captions **.**
- **Check your** spellings **.**
- **Re-write the captions on the lines if you need to.**

First, try without using a dictionary.

Then use a dictionary.

Flat shapes

sq_____

c_____

r_____

_____

_____

_____

tr_____

o_____

st_____

_____

_____

_____

Now try this!

- **Think of two words for solid shapes.**
- **Try to spell them.**
- **Check them. Re-write them.**

Use a dictionary.

Teachers' note Ask the children to identify the shapes on the page and tell them the names of any they do not know. Explain that it does not matter if they spell the words incorrectly; the important thing is to try to spell them for themselves before looking them up in a dictionary. Model how to find words in a dictionary, using its alphabetical structure. For the extension, revise the term 'solid shapes'.

**Developing Literacy
Non-fiction Compendium:
Ages 4–7**
© A & C BLACK

A glossary

- **Read the pages.**

  Which words need to be

  in the | glossary | **?**

- **Underline the words.**

A glossary explains difficult words.

Glass

Glass is transparent.

Rubber

Rubber is waterproof.

Iron and steel

Iron and steel
are magnetic.

Elastic

Elastic stretches.

 Now try this!

- **Choose two of the words.**
- **Write their meanings.**

Use a dictionary.

Teachers' note Before the children begin this activity, they need to have used a glossary in an information book to look up new words. The teacher could model the use of a glossary. Explain that there is no glossary for the 'pages' on the activity sheet and that the children's task is to decide which words need to go in a glossary.

Developing Literacy
Non-fiction Compendium:
Ages 4–7
© A & C BLACK

Topic words: 1

- **Tick your** topic . ✔

Plants		

Food	

Animals	

 Homes	

- **Write your topic words.**

Topic _____

_____   _____

_____   _____

_____   _____

_____   _____

Topic _____

_____   _____

_____   _____

_____   _____

Teachers' note Use this with page 70. The children should work in groups of four, with each child choosing a different topic (they could draw lots or roll a die to decide who chooses first). This page provides one child with record sheets for two games. Discuss the words on the game board (page 70) connected with each topic. Continued on page 70.

Developing Literacy
Non-fiction Compendium:
Ages 4–7
© A & C BLACK

Topic words: 2

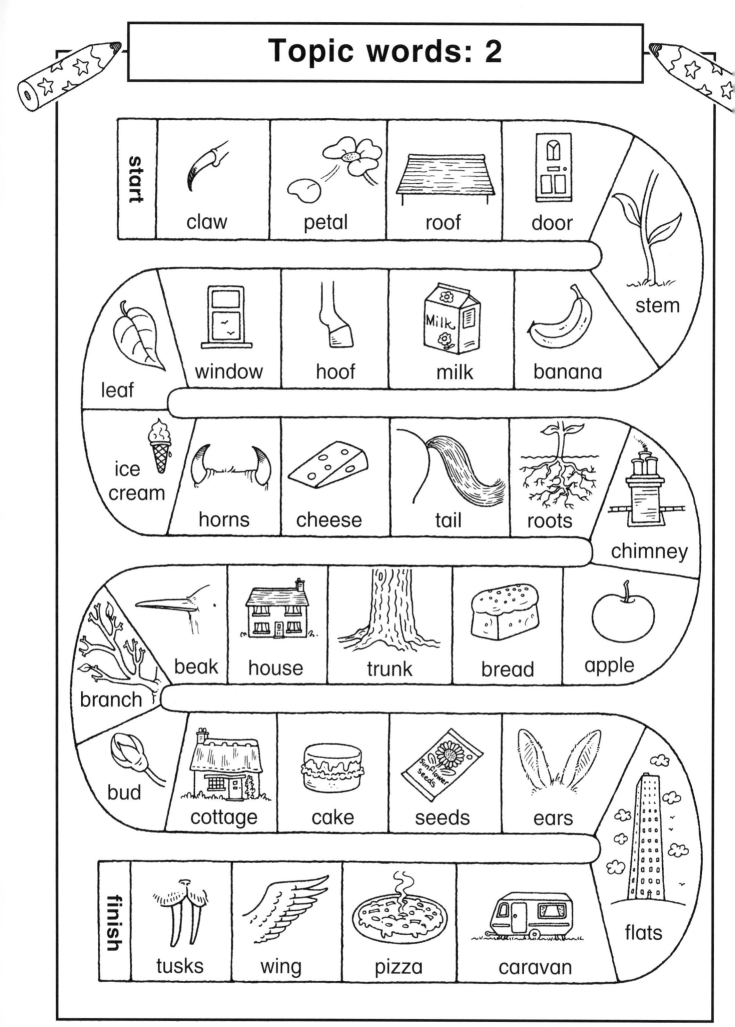

start | claw | petal | roof | door | stem
leaf | window | hoof | milk | banana
ice cream | horns | cheese | tail | roots | chimney
branch | beak | house | trunk | bread | apple
bud | cottage | cake | seeds | ears | flats
finish | tusks | wing | pizza | caravan

Teachers' note Continued from page 69. Each group needs four counters and a die. The children take turns to roll the die. If they land on a word connected with their topic, they write that word on the first record card. If not, they wait until their next turn. The winner is the player with the most words when they have all reached 'finish'.

Developing Literacy
Non-fiction Compendium:
Ages 4–7
© A & C BLACK

Fiction or non-fiction?

Are these books fiction **or** non-fiction **?**

- **Write** f **for fiction. Write** nf **for non-fiction.**

nf

Now try this!

- **Write the title of another** fiction **book.**

- **Write the title of another** non-fiction **book.**

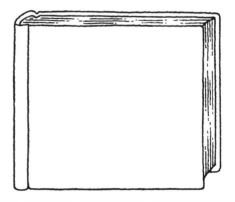

Teachers' note The children could draw the covers of fiction books and non-fiction books they like and glue them onto a display of 'Our favourite books' under the headings 'Fiction' and 'Non-fiction'.

Developing Literacy
Non-fiction Compendium:
Ages 4–7
© A & C BLACK

71

Front cover

- **Label the** `front cover` **of this non-fiction book.**

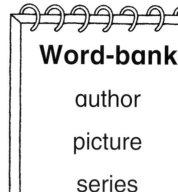
[blank label box]

[blank label box]

Animals

Nicola Edwards

...messages...messages...messages...

[blank label box]

[blank label box]

Now try this!

- **Draw the front cover of another non-fiction book.**
- **Label the important parts.**

Teachers' note Before beginning this activity, the children should have learned the words 'title', 'author', 'picture' and 'series'. Use these words in displays so that they become familiar with the appearance of the words. Point to the words and read them with the children.

Developing Literacy
Non-fiction Compendium:
Ages 4–7
© A & C BLACK

Parts of a page: 1

• **Match the** | picture |, | text | **and** | heading |.

We use our ears to listen to sounds.

We can hear loud and quiet sounds.

We use our eyes to look at things.

We can see big and small things.

We use our nose to smell things.

We can smell good and bad things.

We use our skin to feel things.

We can feel hot and cold things.

We use our tongue to taste things.

We can taste sweet and sour things.

Teachers' note Use this with page 74. The children could work on this activity in groups. Ask them to cut out the text on this sheet and the pictures and headings on the other sheet, then to match up the text with the correct picture and heading. Continued on page 74.

**Developing Literacy
Non-fiction Compendium:
Ages 4–7**
© A & C BLACK

Sight

Taste

Touch

Smell

Hearing

Now try this!

- **Write a** | title | **for the book.**
- **Draw the** | front cover |**.**

Teachers' note Continued from page 73. Provide glue and five separate sheets of paper so that the children can glue each matching heading, text and picture onto a separate page. Encourage them to check that their pages make sense.

Developing Literacy Non-fiction Compendium: Ages 4–7
© A & C BLACK

Which book?

• Choose a book for each child. Draw a line.

 I want to know about plastic.

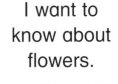 Made from plastic

I want to know about flowers.

 Sun and Moon

I want to know about cars.

 My garden

I want to know about the Moon.

 I want to know about shadows.

 Cars

 My shadow

I want to know about London.

 The London book

• Write one thing you want to find out.

 Now try this!

_____

_____

• Choose a book.

• Write its | title | **.**

Teachers' note Show the children information books. Ask them what the books are about, and how they can tell. Ask them to indicate which book would tell them about, say, plants, pets or magnets. See also page 76, which develops the children's skills in using information books to find specific information.

Developing Literacy
Non-fiction Compendium:
Ages 4–7
© A & C BLACK

Finding out

- **Fill in the gaps.**

Use a non-fiction book.

My topic is _____ **.**

This is my question about it.

_____

_____

_____

Use question words: what, when, how, why, where.

This is the book I will read.

_____

_____

Write the title.

These are the pages I will read.

_____

_____

Write the page numbers.

This is what I found out.

_____

_____

_____

_____

Teachers' note The children should first complete the activity on page 75. This page develops their skills in planning their reading of non-fiction texts: identifying the purpose of their reading by formulating a question, locating the sources they will use and using them to find the answer to the question.

Developing Literacy
Non-fiction Compendium:
Ages 4–7
© A & C BLACK

A fly and a spider

- **Look at the** diagrams .
- **Read the words.**
- **Fill in the gaps.**

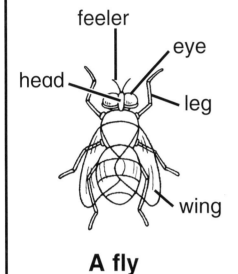

A fly

A fly has ___six___ legs.
It has _____ wings.

On its head it has two _____ and two _____.

A spider has _____ legs.
It has _____ wings.

On its head it has _____ and _____ _____.

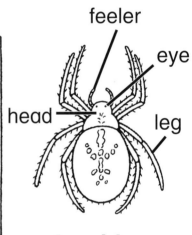

A spider

Now try this!

How is a fly different from a spider?

- **Write two sentences.**

Look at the legs and the wings.

Teachers' note Invite the children to read the labels and to look closely at the pictures before filling in the gaps. Ask them what they can learn from the labelled pictures about a fly and a spider.

**Developing Literacy
Non-fiction Compendium:
Ages 4–7
© A & C BLACK**

Where is it?

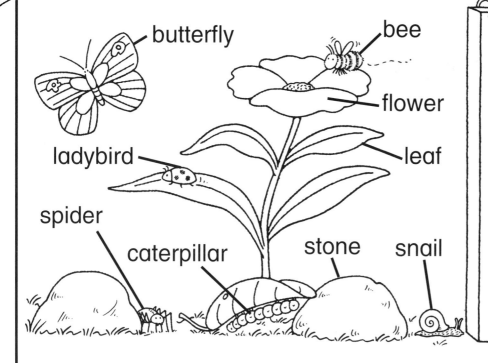

butterfly bee flower leaf ladybird spider caterpillar stone snail

Word-bank

what
where
beside
in
in front of
on
over
under

• **Write three** questions **about the picture.**

1. Where is _____

2. _____

3. _____

• **Write the** answers **to your questions.**

1. _____

2. _____

3. _____

Now try this!

• **Find a picture in an information book.**

• **Write three questions about it.**

• **Give the questions to a friend to answer.**

Teachers' note Invite the children to talk about what they can see in the picture and where the animals are. Revise the words for positions which appear in the word-bank and encourage the children to use them when describing the positions of the animals. Revise the use of question marks.

**Developing Literacy
Non-fiction Compendium:
Ages 4–7**
© A & C BLACK

A hundred years ago

- **Look at the pictures.**
- **Write the missing words.**

Now

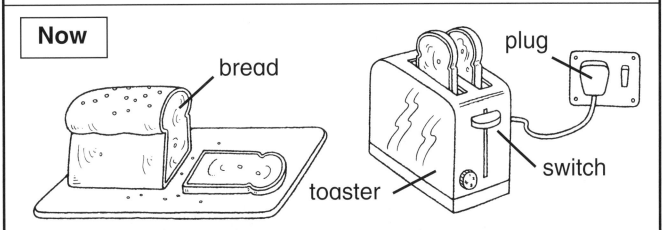

We put the b<u>read</u> in a t_____.

We p_____ in the toaster and s_____ it on.

100 years ago

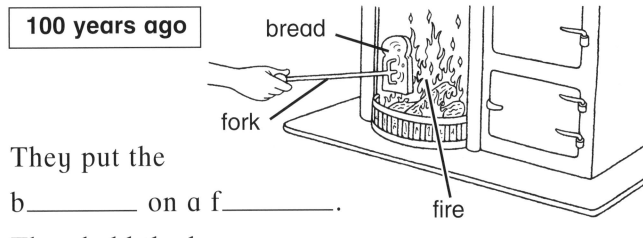

They put the

b_____ on a f_____.

They held the b_____

near the f_____.

- **Write about making tea** now **and** 100 years ago .
- **Draw pictures.**

Word-bank

electric
kettle
teabag
teapot

Teachers' note Read the first text with the children, encouraging them to look at the pictures and read the labels to find out which words are missing. For the extension activity, provide information books. This method of writing information can also be used for work in science and geography.

Developing Literacy
Non-fiction Compendium:
Ages 4–7
© A & C BLACK

Making charts

Do these foods come from animals or plants?

- **Write them on the** chart .

 Use non-fiction books.

bread

cheese

baked beans

milk

orange juice

eggs

apple

sausages

Foods from animals	Foods from plants
cheese	

 Now try this!

- **Find out about four more foods.**
- **Write them on the chart.**

Teachers' note Invite the children to read out the captions, using the pictures and initial phonemes as cues. Ask the children what they know (or think they know) about the foods in the pictures. They can use information books or CD-ROMs to check their ideas.

Developing Literacy
Non-fiction Compendium:
Ages 4–7
© A & C BLACK

Village report

• **Look at the picture map.**

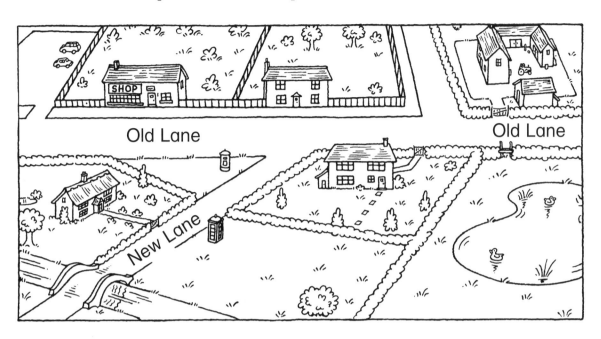

• **Fill in the gaps.**

In the village there are two lanes. They are called

__*Old Lane*__ and _____.

In Old Lane there is a sh_____ and a car p_____.

Beside the sh_____ there is a h_____

and then a f_____. On one side of New

L_____ there is a h_____. On the other

side is a t_____ b_____. There is a

br_____ in New Lane.

• **Write two more sentences about the village.**

Teachers' note You could introduce this activity using a large picture map of an area the children know. Discuss what can be learned about the place from the map and, as a shared writing activity, write a short report about the area.

Developing Literacy
Non-fiction Compendium:
Ages 4–7
© A & C BLACK

Plan a non-fiction book: 1

Title _____

• **Write a** | heading | **for**

each page.

Include a title page, a contents page, a glossary and an index.

Page 1 _Title page_	**Page 2**
Page 3	**Page 4**
Page 5	**Page 6**
Page 7	**Page 8** _Index_

Now try this!

• **Draw a** | cover | **for your book.**

• **Draw and write the** | title page |.

Teachers' note Introduce the activity by looking at a 'big book' version of a non-fiction book and discussing how each page is used. Make a display-sized plan like the one on this page and ask the children how they think the writer's plan of the book would look. Fill in the plan with the children.

Developing Literacy
Non-fiction Compendium:
Ages 4–7
© A & C BLACK

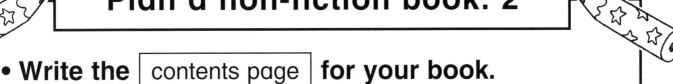

Plan a non-fiction book: 2

• **Write the** contents page **for your book.**

Write the page numbers.

Write the heading for your contents page on this line.

3

Write the page headings.

Now try this!

• **Now write the pages of your book.**

Write the heading on each page.

Teachers' note The children should first complete the activity on page 82. Show them examples of contents pages and invite them to read the headings and the page numbers. Ask why they think the page numbering does not start at 1. (Let them count the number of pages before the contents page.) The children could compile an index as a guided writing activity.

Developing Literacy
Non-fiction Compendium:
Ages 4–7
© A & C BLACK

On the beach

What did they see?

• **Read the words.**

Anna saw a shell.  Mark saw a seagull.

Salim saw some seaweed.

Sara saw a rockpool.

Jack saw some pebbles.   Holly saw a crab.

• **Join the children to the things they saw.**

Anna	crab	pebbles	Sara
Mark	seaweed shell		Jack
Salim	seagull	rockpool	Holly

 **What do you see?**

Now try this!

• **Write** sentences .

 sand   sun   boat

Teachers' note Encourage the children to use the pictures as cues when they attempt any words they cannot read. They could use this page as a model to help them to write a recount of something they have done. The extension activity focuses on the writing of sentences.

Developing Literacy
Non-fiction Compendium:
Ages 4–7
© A & C BLACK

That's not right!

- ## Write the sentences in the correct order.

 I got dressed.

 I got up.

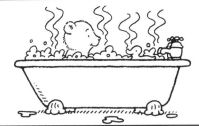 I had a bath.

 I took off my pyjamas.

_____

_____

_____

_____

_____

 • **Write the next sentence.**

Use a dictionary.

Teachers' note You could introduce this activity by making a copy of a simple recount and cutting it up into separate sentences. Ask the children to put the sentences into the correct order and then to check this against the original. See also page 86, which introduces the connective words used in recounts.

Developing Literacy
Non-fiction Compendium:
Ages 4–7
© A & C BLACK

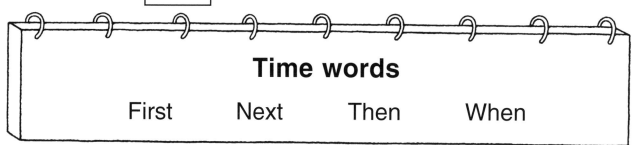

- **Read the** `time` **words.**

Time words

| First | Next | Then | When |

- **Learn the time words.**

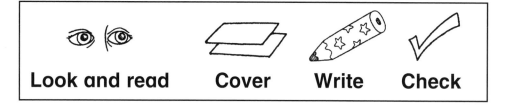

Look and read   **Cover**   **Write**   **Check**

- **Fill in the gaps.**

Making toast

_____ I got some bread.

_____ I put the bread in the toaster.

_____ I switched it on.

_____ the toast was ready it popped up.

- **Write the next sentence.**

Use `after that` .

Use a dictionary.

Teachers' note The children should first complete the activity on page 85. They could look for 'time words' in other recounts they read and introduce them into their own writing.

Developing Literacy
Non-fiction Compendium:
Ages 4–7
© A & C BLACK

What did you do?

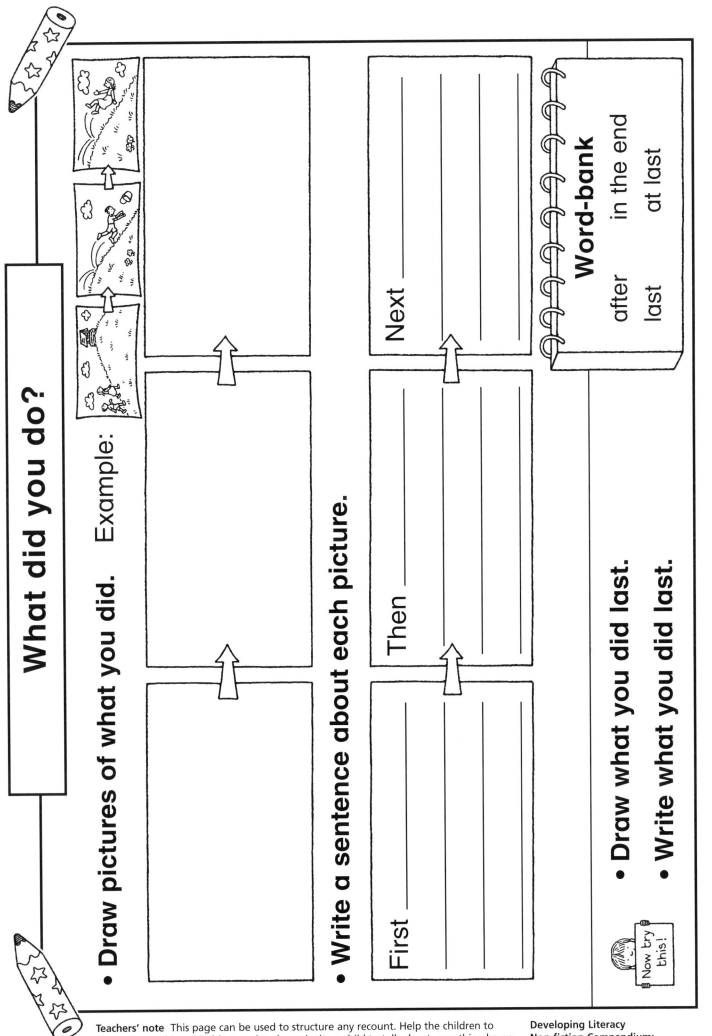

- **Draw pictures of what you did.**   Example:

- **Write a sentence about each picture.**

First _____

Then _____

Next _____

Word-bank

after   in the end   at last

last

- **Draw what you did last.**
- **Write what you did last.**

Now try this!

Teachers' note This page can be used to structure any recount. Help the children to think of something suitable to write about; invite a child to talk about something he or she has done. Fill in an enlarged version of the page for what the child says. Point out the words 'First', 'Then' and 'Next'. With the children, read what you have written.

Developing Literacy
Non-fiction Compendium:
Ages 4–7
© A & C BLACK

87

Notes on the activities

The notes below expand upon those provided at the bottom of the activity pages. They give ideas and suggestions for making the most of the activity sheet, including suggestions for the whole-class introduction, the plenary session or for follow-up work using an adapted version of the sheet. The activities are grouped into units in line with the Primary Framework for Literacy, but the pages need not be presented in the order in which they appear, unless stated otherwise.

Unit 1: Instructions

The activities in this section reinforce the children's skills in word recognition, word structure and spelling and sentence structure and develop their ability to read, use and understand the structure and language style of instructions. They are encouraged to write instructions for different purposes: for example, for getting from place to place, for playing games, for carrying out everyday activities and for cooking things. The children learn to plan their writing with the help of frameworks and models and to base their own writing on non-fiction texts they have read.

Car park machine (page 93). This activity develops the children's skills in reading instructions. Encourage them to use the pictures as cues to help them to read any words they do not know and to use the critical features of the words, such as familiar letter combinations (for example 'ou' and 'ch'). Read out the following sentences and ask the children whether they are instructions: 'I put my ticket in the machine,' 'I read how much to pay,' and 'I put my money in the slot.' Ask them to explain how they know (they do not tell people what to do).

Make a chain of people and **Learn to cut wood** (pages 94–95). These activities develop the children's ability to recognise the critical features of instructions: a statement of purpose at the beginning, followed by a list of things needed, and then a step-by-step list of things to do (which uses direct language), along with diagrams to help to explain them.

A journey (page 96). In this activity the children work out how to direct someone who wants to travel from one town to another using a combination of walking and travelling by bus and train. Before the activity you could take the children for a walk in the local area. As you walk, talk about the direction you are taking and the things you pass. Afterwards, describe the walk together: for example, 'We turned right at the school gate and walked along …' Ask the children to change what they say into instructions (to tell someone else what to do). They could also write, and check for accuracy, instructions for visitors to the school.

Grotty soup (page 97). This activity presents a comic picture from which the children are required to gather information to write a recipe. They could check one another's recipes for omissions and for any parts which are in the wrong order.

Snakes and ladders and **Sending a letter** (pages 98–99). These activities provide the children with a structure to help them to write instructions for familiar processes in the correct order and including all the important details.

Follow a diagram (page 100). This activity helps the children to use labelled drawings to convey information. For lower-achieving children, you could cut out the diagram for them to glue onto a large piece of paper, allowing space for them to write their instructions next to the appropriate parts of it. Before the children begin the activity, they should look at labelled diagrams and pictures in books and notice how the diagrams are labelled: the labels are sometimes written in boxes and they are usually linked by lines to the parts they name. Their instructions could be displayed for others to follow, then evaluate and suggest improvements.

Instruction words (page 101). This activity focuses on the language of instructions. The children examine the changes they need to make in order to change a statement into an instruction. Similarly, they could convert into instructions any recounts they have previously written of things made during design and technology or art lessons.

Unit 2: Explanations

In this section, the children reinforce their understanding of the features of non-fiction books (contents page, glossary, index, diagrams, etc.) and explore explanatory texts whose purpose is to provide the answers to questions. They learn to use frameworks and models to write their own explanations based on non-fiction texts they have read.

Use the index (page 102). This activity develops the children's skills in using an index for a purpose. They use the index of an information book to locate the pages on which they are likely to find the answers to questions. Useful information books for this activity include *Eyewitness Explorers: Weather* (John Farndon, Dorling Kindersley) and *Usborne Spotters' Guides: The*

Weather (Frances Wilson and Felicity Mansfield, Usborne). When introducing the activity, it is useful to help the children to identify the key word in each question: for example, 'fog', 'clouds' and 'lightning'. Lower-achieving children may wish to copy the key word onto a strip of paper and move it down the index until they find the word which matches it.

Use the glossary (page 103). This activity encourages the children to use information books effectively, by looking up technical vocabulary connected with a topic. You could ask them questions about the information in the glossary: for example, 'What is the difference between a pond and a lake?', 'How is a river different from a canal?' and 'How is a mountain different from a hill?'

Fairground glossary (page 104). This activity reinforces the children's skills in finding information from non-fiction texts, while developing their vocabulary. They could make glossaries for other collections, such as hats, shoes, mammals, reptiles, insects, countries and cities. This could be linked with sentence structure work on nouns.

Use a flow-chart (page 105). This activity introduces the use of a flow-chart and diagrams in an explanation. Before they begin the activity, the children could read flow-charts in information books and then explain, in their own words, the process described in them.

A giant's flow-chart (page 106). This activity provides a framework to help the children to write an explanation. The questions encourage them to organise their explanation and could be used as the basis for headings.

Use a diagram (page 107). In this activity the children learn when it is appropriate to use a cyclical diagram in an explanation. They could first read other cyclical charts in science information books: for example, life-cycles of animals or plants and the water cycle. Discuss the important features of a cyclical diagram (labelled illustrations, boxes and arrows) and point out that it has no beginning or end. Ask the children if they can explain why not.

Making notes: 1 and **2** (pages 108–109). These pages develop the children's skills in making notes as quickly and accurately as possible (using standard abbreviations). They also practise identifying the parts of a text which are relevant to their questions. The activities discourage the children from copying out large pieces of text and help them to write 'in their own words'.

Unit 3: Information texts

In this section, the children consolidate their knowledge of how dictionaries and other reference books are organised and explore the differences between fiction and non-fiction books. They learn how to decide whether or not a non-fiction book will provide the information they want, then to scan the book to find that information and to skim-read the text before deciding which parts to read in detail. The concept of 'definitions' is introduced to encourage them to think about meaning as they read.

Use a dictionary (page 110). This activity shows the children how to use a dictionary efficiently to check spellings. Point out useful features in a dictionary such as alphabetical markers on the top, bottom or outside edge of the pages, and the guide words in bold (or in colour) at the tops of the pages. On an alphabet strip displayed in the classroom, the children could indicate where the words belong. They could write words they come across in their reading on strips of paper and fix them onto the correct sections of the alphabet line. Encourage them to use a dictionary routinely to check words they are not sure how to spell.

Look it up (page 111). This activity focuses on using a dictionary to find the meanings of words. In order to answer the questions, the children have to think about what they read in the dictionary definitions (which is not necessarily required when they merely look up and write out the meanings of words).

Definitions: 1 and **2** (pages 112–113). These pages reinforce the children's understanding of 'definitions' and give practice in using a dictionary. They may know some of the words in **Definitions: 1** but should use a dictionary to check that their understanding is correct.

Joke dictionary: 1 and **2** (pages 114–115). These pages develop the children's understanding of definitions and of how dictionaries are organised. They could make a class 'joke dictionary' of 'silly definitions' using a scrap book in which the pages are lettered from A to Z.

Bo Peep's address book (page 116). This activity is based on a familiar alphabetically ordered text – an address book. You could introduce it by reading an enlarged copy of a real address book as a shared text. The entries are ordered by first letter only, since the user adds them to the next available space on the appropriate page. Let the children look at a collection of address books and talk about the features which make them easy to use, such as letter tabs at the edges of the pages or indented pages on which the initial letter can be seen without opening the book. The children could make their own address books and write in the addresses of their friends and family. You could introduce alphabetical order by both first and second letter by investigating what happens in a dictionary or other alphabetical list where two words begin with the same letter.

Fact or fiction? (page 117). This activity helps the children to distinguish between fact and fiction. They could write definitions of 'fact' and 'fiction' for display in the class library, with hints to help others to decide whether a piece of text is fact or fiction. Useful words and phrases for this exercise include: 'real', 'made-up', 'invented', 'true' and 'can be proved'.

Non-fiction features (page 118). This activity reinforces the differences between fiction and non-fiction books. Revise the terms 'fiction' and 'non-fiction' and invite different children to choose a fiction book or non-fiction book from a collection. Ask them how they can tell what kind of book it is, and point out the distinctive features of non-fiction books: the kind of title and front cover illustration, the back cover blurb, the contents page, the glossary and index and the layout of pages (including features such as labelled diagrams and charts).

What I know and **Questions and answers** (pages 119–120). These activities help the children to prepare for reading non-fiction for a purpose which is clear to them. They encourage them to use information books to find specific pieces of information, having talked about what they already know about a topic. These sheets also allow the teacher to assess the children's understanding of a new topic in another subject (for example, science or geography) prior to beginning work on it. **Questions and answers** develops the children's skills in formulating questions before they read information texts. This process encourages them to use the texts to find specific information. The teacher can model how to evaluate information books with regard to their usefulness for answering a specific question by demonstrating how to check the contents page and index and then how to use them to locate the information. The children could go on to write the answers to their questions but the emphasis here is on preparation for reading.

Skim a text (page 121). This activity helps the children to use non-fiction books efficiently. Having decided what they want to find out, they learn to appraise books quickly, checking whether they are going to be helpful before they begin to read them. They could keep a checklist to hand when looking for information in any subject, reminding them to look at the title, contents page, headings, sub-headings, illustrations and index.

Find the information (page 122). This activity offers a useful strategy for reading for information. Rather than reading an information book from cover to cover, the children learn the steps to take to find the relevant parts of the book.

Text scan (page 123). This helps the children to develop the ability to scan a piece of text in order to find the relevant information efficiently.

Unit 4: Non-chronological reports

In this section, the children learn to use plans, notes, charts and writing frameworks to prepare for and then write non-chronological reports.

Bring and buy sale (page 124). This activity develops the children's understanding of how plans can be useful. Discuss what might happen at the bring and buy sale if there were no plan (you could ask them how the children holding the sale would know what to ask people to bring to the sale, where each stall should be, what would be sold at each stall and who should look after it).

Gran's schooldays: 1 and **2** (pages 125–126). These pages show how notes can be written quickly to help the children to remember the information they have gathered. The activities also demonstrate how questions can be turned into sub-headings to support the organisation of a non-chronological report. Ask the children to choose questions they have written in preparation for reading about particular topics, then to turn the questions into sub-headings.

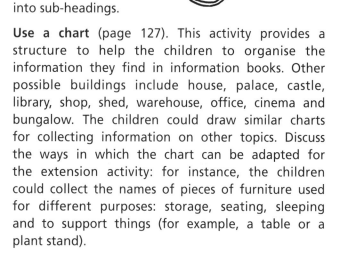

Use a chart (page 127). This activity provides a structure to help the children to organise the information they find in information books. Other possible buildings include house, palace, castle, library, shop, shed, warehouse, office, cinema and bungalow. The children could draw similar charts for collecting information on other topics. Discuss the ways in which the chart can be adapted for the extension activity: for instance, the children could collect the names of pieces of furniture used for different purposes: storage, seating, sleeping and to support things (for example, a table or a plant stand).

Write a report (page 128). This activity involves planning and writing a non-chronological report. The children could first read a non-chronological report about a place, but with some of the words masked. Ask them to supply the missing words.

Learning objectives

The following chart shows how the Ages 6–7 activity sheets (pages 93–128) match the learning objectives addressed by the Year 2 units in the Non-fiction block of the Primary Framework for Literacy. (Where a page number is shown in bold type, this indicates the learning objective is the main focus of the activity.)

Objectives	Unit 1: Instructions	Unit 2: Explanations	Unit 3: Information texts	Unit 4: Non-chronological reports
Speaking				
Explain ideas and processes using imaginative and adventurous vocabulary and non-verbal gestures to support communication		104, 106		
Word recognition: decoding (reading) and encoding (spelling)				
Read independently and with increasing fluency longer and less familiar texts	93	102, 103, 109	117, 118, 121, 122	
Spell with increasing accuracy and confidence, drawing on word recognition and knowledge of word structure and spelling patterns	97–101	102–104, 106–109	110–113, 116, 121–123	125–127
Know how to tackle unfamiliar words which are not completely decodable	93, 95–97, 99	102–104, 106–109	110–118, 121–123	124, 127, 128
Read and spell less common alternative graphemes including trigraphs	93, 95–98, 100	102, 104, 106, 108, 109	112, 114, 115, 123	125, 127, 128
Read high and medium frequency words independently and automatically	93–101	102–109	110–115, 117, 121, 122	107, 124–128
Word structure and spelling				
Spell with increasing accuracy and confidence, drawing on word recognition and knowledge of word structure, and spelling patterns including common inflections and use of double letters	97–101	102–104, 106, 108, 109	**110**, 111–113, **114**, **115**, 118	125–128
Read and spell less common alternative graphemes including trigraphs	93, 95–98, 100	104, 106, 108, 109	112, 114, 115, 123	125, 127, 128

Objectives	Unit 1: Instructions	Unit 2: Explanations	Unit 3: Information texts	Unit 4: Non-chronological reports
Understanding and interpreting texts				
Draw together ideas and information from across a whole text, using simple signposts in the text	**93, 94, 95, 96**	**102, 103, 104,** 107, **108, 109**	107, 110–113, 116, 118, **121, 122, 123**	**124**, 125
Give some reasons why things happen or characters change		102, 106, 109		
Explain organisational features of texts, including alphabetical order, layout, diagrams, captions, hyperlinks and bullet points	97	102, **105, 106, 107**	107, 110, 112, 114, 115, **116**, 118, 121–123	
Engaging with and responding to texts				
Explain their reactions to texts, commenting on important aspects			**117, 118**, 121, 123	
Creating and shaping texts				
Draw on knowledge and experience of texts in deciding and planning what and how to write	**97, 98, 99, 100, 101**	104–106, 108, 109		**125, 126**, 128
Maintain consistency in non-narrative, including purpose and tense	96–101	104, 106–108		125, 126, 128
Make adventurous word and language choices appropriate to style and purpose of text		105	**111, 112, 113,** 114, 115	
Select from different presentational features to suit particular writing purposes on paper and on screen	99	104–106, 108, 109		
Text structure and organisation				
Use planning to establish clear sections for writing	99	104, 106, 108, 109	**119, 120**, 123	125, 126, **127, 128**
Sentence structure and punctuation				
Write simple and compound sentences and begin to use subordination in relation to time and reason	97–99	106		
Compose sentences using tense consistently (present and past)	96–101	104, 106–108		126, 128

Car park machine

• **Read the** instructions .

1. Put your ticket in the slot.

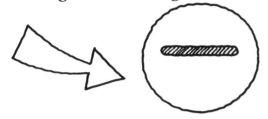

2. Read how much to pay.

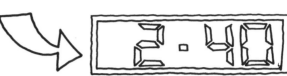

3. Put your money in the slot.

You can use these coins: £1, 50p, 20p, 10p, 5p.

No change given.

• **Answer the questions. Write** yes **or** no .

1. Do you need a ticket?

2. Is there a slot to put the ticket in?

3. Do you put the money in the same slot as the ticket?

4. Can you pay with 2p coins?

5. Can you pay with a £5 note?

6. Does change come out of a slot?

Now try this!

What else might you need to know about the car park?

This time, the answers will <u>not</u> be **yes** or **no**.

• **Write three questions. Use** how , what **and** where .

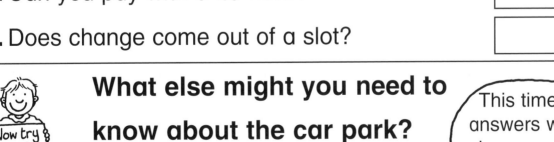

Teachers' note Ask the children if they have seen car park machines into which people insert money to pay for parking. Talk about how different machines work. Draw attention to the language of command used in instructions ('Put...', 'Read...' and so on).

Developing Literacy
Non-fiction Compendium:
Ages 4–7
© A & C BLACK

Make a chain of people

• **Follow the** | instructions | .

Use the pictures to help you.

How to make a chain of people

You need:

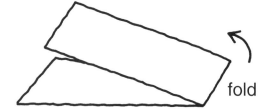

a pencil   a strip of paper   scissors

1.

fold

Fold the paper in half.

2.

fold

Fold the paper in half again.

3.

fold

Fold the paper in half again.

4.

Draw half a person on the fold.

5.

Do not cut along the folds!

Cut along the lines.

6.

Open out the chain of people.

Now try this!

• **Write about how easy or difficult it was to follow the instructions.**

Teachers' note You could introduce this activity by writing some simple instructions on the board: for example, for making sounds using a comb and tissue paper. The children could take turns to read out parts of the instructions for you to follow. Ask them to check that you do as they say (you could make some deliberate mistakes).

**Developing Literacy
Non-fiction Compendium:
Ages 4–7
© A & C BLACK**

Learn to cut wood

- **Cut out the** instructions.
- **Put them in order.**

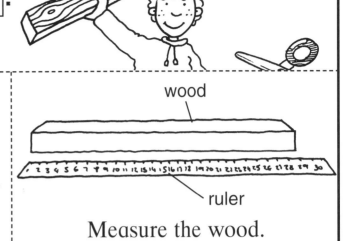

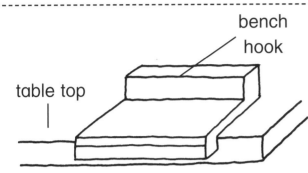

Put the bench hook on the table top.

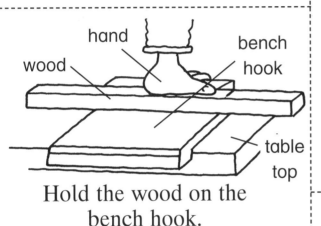

Hold the wood on the bench hook.

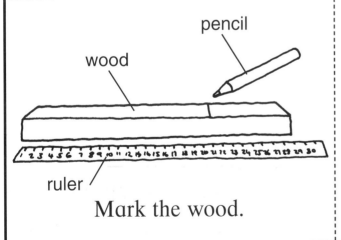

Mark the wood.

Measure the wood.

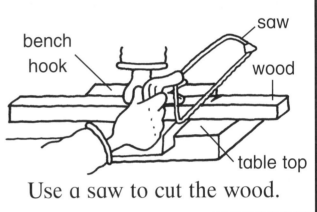

Use a saw to cut the wood.

How to cut a piece of wood

You need:

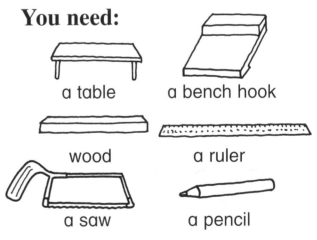

a table   a bench hook

wood   a ruler

a saw   a pencil

- **Write a safety warning for the instructions.**

Teachers' note Show the children the equipment depicted on the page and talk about how it is used (this might serve as an introduction to, or revision on, using these tools in design and technology lessons). Label and display the tools, so that the children can refer to them as they re-order the instructions.

Developing Literacy
Non-fiction Compendium:
Ages 4–7
© A & C BLACK

A journey

- **Look at the** map **and the** key **. They show how Greg goes to visit his cousin Lisa.**

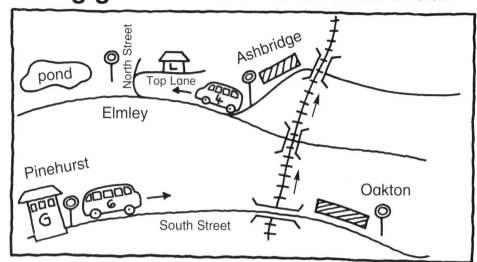

- **Write** instructions **for Greg.**

1. From your house, walk along ___South___ Street to the _____ _____.

2. Take the number ___ bus to _____.

3. Get off the _____ at the railway _____.

4. Take the _____ to _____.

5. Take the number ___ _____ from Ashbridge railway station to _____.

6. Get off the bus at _____ Street.

7. Cross the road and turn right into _____.

- **Write instructions for Lisa to go to Greg's house.**

You might need to turn the map upside-down.

Teachers' note It will be helpful to revise the use of keys, and to invite the children to describe what they can see on the map. For lower-achieving children, you could add words to the skeleton instructions; for higher-achieving children, you may wish to delete some of those provided.

Developing Literacy Non-fiction Compendium: Ages 4–7 © A & C BLACK

Grotty soup

Mr Grott is making a cauldron of grotty soup.

...and 200 grams of mud...

...and a cupful of pond water.

2 litres of slime and 1 litre of sludge should be enough.

We need to add a pinch of soil, then boil it for an hour.

Then we'll sprinkle grated toenails onto the soup.

- **Write the recipe for Mr Grott's soup.**

Ingredients:

2 litres slime

Method: Put the slime and

- **Write a recipe for grotty sandwiches.**

Teachers' note The children should first read some recipes and notice their key features: a list of ingredients and, sometimes, equipment, followed by step-by-step instructions which use direct language to tell the reader what to do. You could introduce the activity by inviting a group of children to read the parts of 'the Grotts' and the narrator.

Developing Literacy
Non-fiction Compendium:
Ages 4–7
© A & C BLACK

Snakes and ladders

- **Look at the pictures.**

- **Read the labels and captions.**

- **Complete the** | instructions |.

1. Roll the _die_____.

2. Look at the _____. Move that number of squares.

3. If you _____,

go _____.

4. If you _____,

go _____.

5. Give the _____ and the _____ to

the _____.

6. The winner _____.

- **Draw pictures for another game.**

- **Write instructions.**

Teachers' note This could be introduced by reading the instructions for another familiar game as a shared text. Discuss the important features of instructions for games: telling the readers, step-by-step, what to do, what they should do if different things happen in the game, how their turn ends and how to win.

Developing Literacy
Non-fiction Compendium:
Ages 4–7
© A & C BLACK

Sending a letter

- **Write** | instructions | **for sending a letter.**

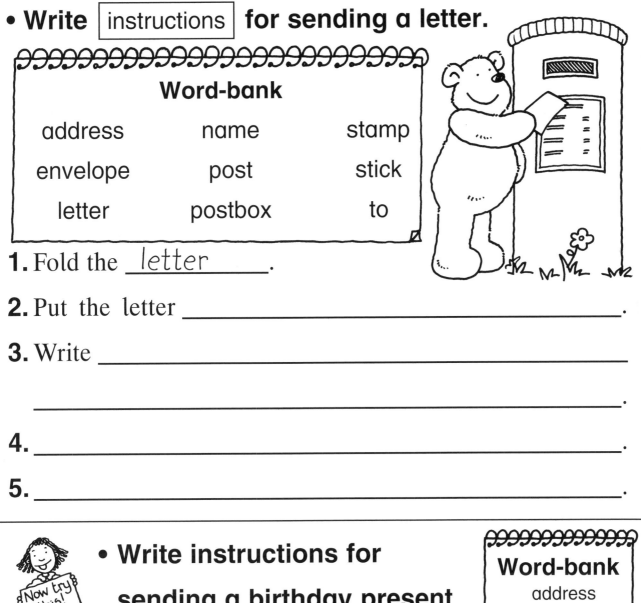

Word-bank

address	name	stamp
envelope	post	stick
letter	postbox	to

1. Fold the _letter_ .

2. Put the letter _____ .

3. Write _____

_____ .

4. _____ .

5. _____ .

- **Write instructions for sending a birthday present.**

_____

_____

_____

_____

_____

Word-bank

address

from

label

name

paper

post office

stick

sticky tape

take

to

wrap

write

Teachers' note It may be useful for the children first to act out the process of sending a letter, while telling a friend what they are doing. Before the extension activity they could act out the wrapping and sending of a present. As a further extension activity, ask the children to write instructions for sending e-mails to pen-friends in other schools.

Developing Literacy
Non-fiction Compendium:
Ages 4–7
© A & C BLACK

Follow a diagram

- **Label the diagram.**
- **Complete the** `instructions` **for making the circuit.**

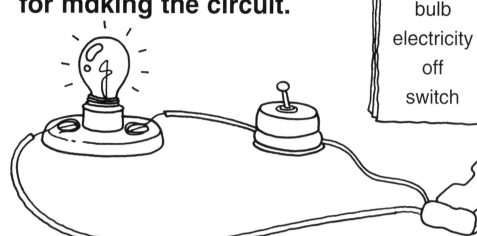

You need: _a bulb,_ _____

_____

_____

1. _Join_ one wire from the battery-holder to the _____.

2. Join the other wire to the _____.

3. Join a wire from the switch to the _____.

4. Screw a bulb into the _____.

5. Switch on _____.

Now try this!

- **Write three questions about the diagram.**
- **Give them to a friend to answer.**

For example:
How many bulbs
do I need?

Teachers' note The children first need experience of using a simple circuit with a switch. Discuss the words in the word-bank; you could show the children the equipment as a reminder. Invite them to explain what happens when they switch on and off. Their explanations need not involve scientific knowledge at great depth, but could be based simply on their observations.

**Developing Literacy
Non-fiction Compendium:
Ages 4–7
© A & C BLACK**

Instruction words

- **Read how Emma made a magnetic fishing set.**

1.  I drew 10 fish.	**2.**  I cut out the fish.
3. 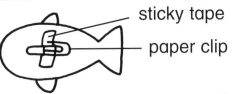 sticky tape — paper clip I taped a paper clip onto each fish.	**4.** 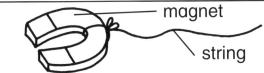 magnet — string I tied a piece of string onto a magnet.

Turn Emma's writing into instructions .

- **Underline the words you need to change.**

- **Write the instructions.**

 Do not use the word 'I'.

How to make a magnetic fishing set

You need: _a pencil,_ _____

_____

1. Draw _____

2. _____

3. _____

4. _____

 • **Write instructions for playing the game.**

Teachers' note Read to the class the recount about making a magnetic fishing set. Ask the children if it sounds like a set of instructions (whether it tells the reader what to do). Model how to change the first sentence to direct language. For the extension activity, remind the children to start each sentence with an instruction word.

Developing Literacy
Non-fiction Compendium:
Ages 4–7
© A & C BLACK

Use the index

You need an information book about weather.

- List the pages which will help you to answer the questions.

Underline the important words in each question.

Then look them up in the index.

Question	Pages
Where does fog come from?	
How are clouds made?	
What makes some clouds black?	
What happens when lightning strikes a building?	
What makes it rain?	
What makes the noise of thunder?	
What makes the wind blow?	
What is the shape of a snowflake?	

- Write two more questions about weather.

1. _____

2. _____

- On which pages can you find the answers?

Question 1 _____ Question 2 _____

- Write the answers to your two questions.

Teachers' note Show the children the index page of an information book and discuss its purpose. Model how to use the index to find information in answer to a question. Explain how the index is organised to make words easy to find and to show the pages on which they are mentioned. The same information book can be used for the extension activity as for the main activity.

**Developing Literacy
Non-fiction Compendium:
Ages 4–7
© A & C BLACK**

Use the glossary

- **Find these words in the** glossary.

- **Underline them.**

- **Write the glossary word.**

a waterway ___canal___   a road _____

very high land _____   moving water _____

low land _____   a crop _____

wet land _____   land with trees _____

Glossary

canal <u>A waterway</u> which has been built as a route for transport.
forest A large area of land with trees.
hill A high piece of land (not as high as a mountain).
lake A large area of still water.
marsh A piece of very wet land.
motorway A road for traffic only.
mountain A very high piece of land.

oats A cereal crop, grown in fields for food.
pond A small area of still, fresh water.
river A large stream of moving water which flows through a valley until it joins another river, a lake or the sea.
valley A long piece of low land between hills or mountains.

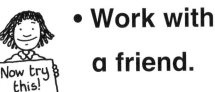

- **Work with a friend.**

You each need a book with a glossary.

- **Write four words from your glossary.**

- **Ask your friend to find their meanings in the glossary.**

Teachers' note Provide information books with glossaries and model how to use the glossary to find the meaning of a word. It is useful to point out that a glossary, like a dictionary, gives definitions of words which are arranged in alphabetical order, but that it is easier to use than a dictionary because it gives only words included in that book.

Developing Literacy
Non-fiction Compendium:
Ages 4–7
© A & C BLACK

Fairground glossary

- **Think of different kinds of fairground rides.**
- **Write the name of each** Work in pairs! **ride on a glossary card.**
- **Write a** definition **. Draw a picture.**
- **Put the cards in alphabetical order.**

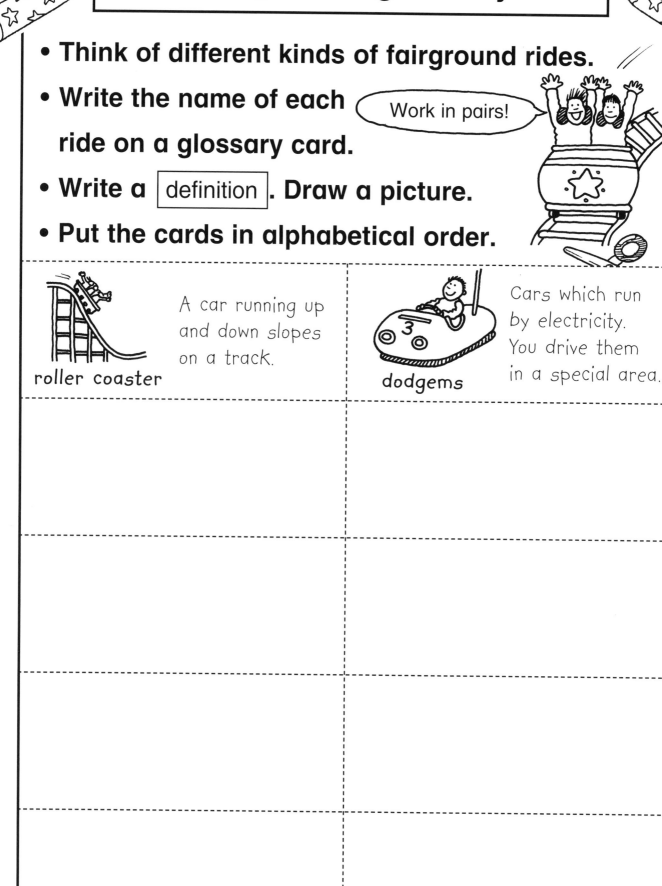

roller coaster — A car running up and down slopes on a track.

dodgems — Cars which run by electricity. You drive them in a special area.

Teachers' note You could introduce this activity by showing the children pictures of fairground rides and asking if they know what they are called. Label the pictures. The children could look for others in information books; encourage them to select books they think will help them.

Developing Literacy
Non-fiction Compendium:
Ages 4–7
© A & C BLACK

Use a flow-chart

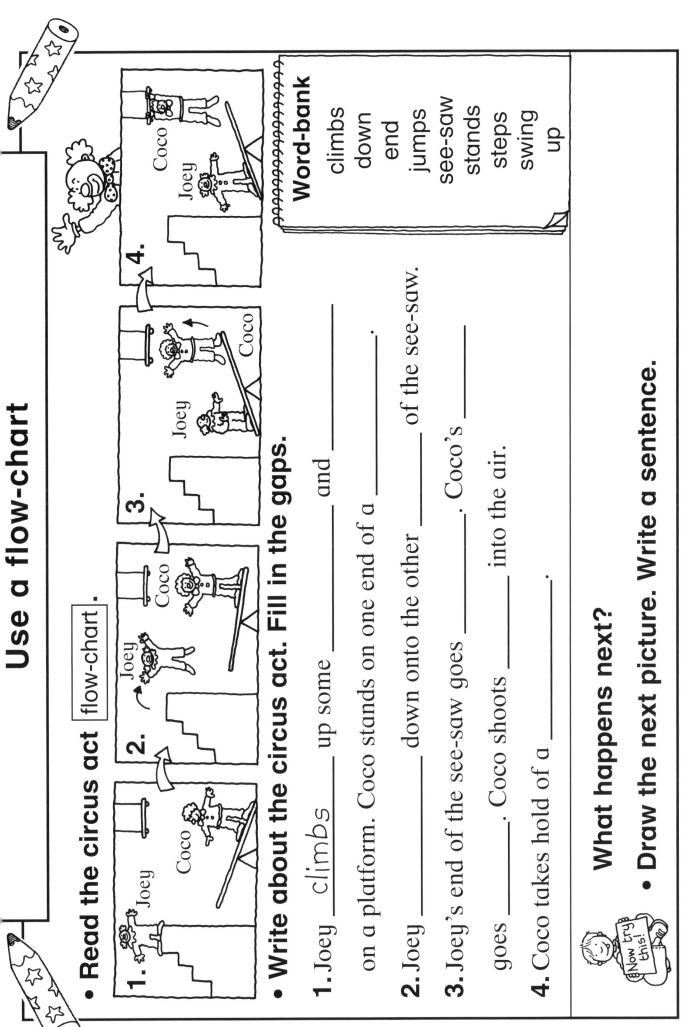

• **Read the circus act** flow-chart.

Word-bank
climbs
down
end
jumps
see-saw
stands
steps
swing
up

• **Write about the circus act. Fill in the gaps.**

1. Joey _climbs_ up some _____ and _____ on a platform. Coco stands on one end of a _____.

2. Joey _____ down onto the other _____ of the see-saw.

3. Joey's end of the see-saw goes _____. Coco's _____ goes _____. Coco shoots _____ into the air.

4. Coco takes hold of a _____ _____.

What happens next?

• **Draw the next picture. Write a sentence.**

Now try this!

Teachers' note Ask the children to describe orally what the clowns do. Encourage them to use accurate vocabulary, such as 'lands', 'see-saw', 'jumps' and 'swing' (or 'trapeze'). Point out the causes and effects of what happens: for example, Coco's end of the see-saw goes up because Joey lands on the other end.

Developing Literacy
Non-fiction Compendium:
Ages 4–7
© A & C BLACK

105

A giant's flow-chart

- **Design a 'people trap' for the giant.**

- **Draw pictures. Write labels and notes.**

- **Tell a friend how the trap works.**

Fee, fi, fo, fum...

What does the trap look like?

How can I hide it?

How do I make sure people go into it?

How do I stop them getting out?

What should the giant do next?

- **Draw and write the next part of the** flow-chart .

Teachers' note Discuss what the children know about giants in stories. Ask them how a giant could set a trap to catch people and draw their attention to the questions on this page, which will help them to organise their flow-chart.

Developing Literacy
Non-fiction Compendium:
Ages 4–7
© A & C BLACK

Use a diagram

- **Look at the** `life-cycle` **of a tomato.**
- **Read the sentences about each part of the** `diagram` **. Fill in the gaps.**

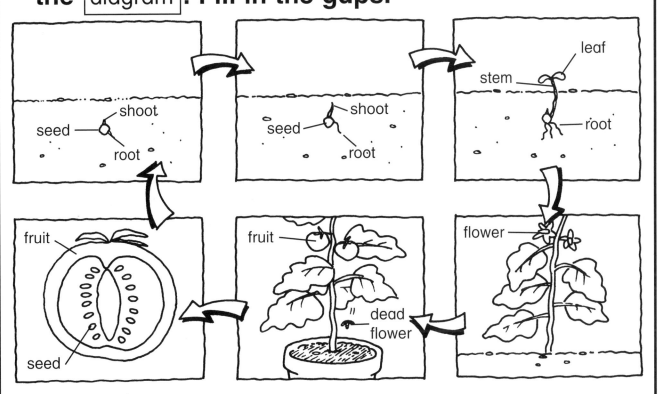

a. A <u>root</u> grows downwards from the _____.

b. A shoot _____ upwards from the _____.

c. Leaves grow _____.

d. The stem grows _____ and flowers _____

_____.

e. The flowers die and _____. Fruit _____

_____.

f. Inside the fruit _____

_____.

Teachers' note At the start of the activity, help the children to explain orally what happens as the tomato plant grows. Ensure the children understand the continuous nature of the cycle. Encourage them to use the vocabulary provided on this page and to say in which direction the root and the shoot grow. You could write the words 'upwards' and 'downwards' on the board.

Developing Literacy
Non-fiction Compendium:
Ages 4–7
© A & C BLACK

- **Write the** [information] **in the shortest way you can.**

You can miss out words like me, I, we and my.

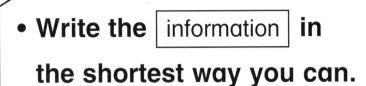

Shortened words

afternoon	pm
and	+
evening	pm
football	f'ball
morning	am
seven	7
Sunday	Sun
to	→

I went to the park on Sunday.

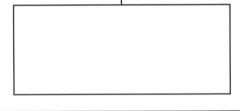

Sun – went → park

In the morning I played football with my Mum.

After that we had fish and chips for lunch.

In the afternoon we went to visit my Gran.

We got home at seven o'clock in the evening.

Now try this!

- **Make notes about something you have done.**

Use shortened words.

Teachers' note Discuss the purpose of making notes and point out that notes are meant to be written quickly, for personal use, to be written up later for others to read. You could show the children examples of good and bad note-making: good notes can be read and understood later; bad notes cannot. Point out that in notes it is quicker not to write full sentences.

**Developing Literacy
Non-fiction Compendium:
Ages 4–7
© A & C BLACK**

- **Read Sunhil's question.**
- **Read the** report .
- **Underline the parts which will help Sunhil to answer the question.**

How do fish breathe?

Fish are cold-blooded. This means that the body of a fish has the same temperature as the water around it. A fish's body is covered with scales.

All <u>animals need a gas called oxygen</u>. There is <u>oxygen in the air and in water</u>. People, and many other animals, use their lungs to breathe in oxygen from the air. In their lungs oxygen passes into the blood.

The heart pumps the blood, with the oxygen in it, around the body.

A fish does not have lungs. It cannot breathe in oxygen from the air. Instead, it has gills behind its head. Water goes into the fish's mouth, over the gills and back out through the gills. In the gills, oxygen is taken from the water into the blood.

- **Make notes about how fish breathe.**

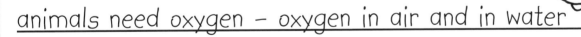

animals need oxygen – oxygen in air and in water

_____

_____

_____

- **Cover the report.**

Use your notes.

- **Write an** explanation **of how fish breathe.**

Teachers' note The children should first complete the activity on page 108. Explain that this activity is about finding the information needed to answer a question, and about making notes only on the words and phrases which will help them. Remind the children that notes need to be written in the shortest and quickest way possible. They could compare their notes with the sentences in the report.

Developing Literacy
Non-fiction Compendium:
Ages 4–7
© A & C BLACK

Use a dictionary

- ## Look up the words.
- ## Complete the chart.
- ## Write the correct spellings in the last column.

Word	Where will you look? front / middle / back	Is the spelling correct? ✓ X	Correct spelling
bear	front		
camel			
zebera			
monky			
sheap			
rabit			
aligator			
lion			

Now try this!

- ## Write four words which you are not sure how to spell.

  _____ _____ _____ _____

- ## Look them up in a │ dictionary │.
- ## Write the correct spellings.

  _____ _____ _____ _____

Teachers' note Show the children a simple dictionary and ask them where you should open it to find, say, 'zip' (near the front/back/middle). Ask them how they know. Do the same with other examples and model how to find each word (by its first letter) within the chosen section. For the extension activity, emphasise that it does not matter if the children spell the words incorrectly the first time they write them.

**Developing Literacy
Non-fiction Compendium:
Ages 4–7
© A & C BLACK**

Look it up

- **Look at the chart.**
- **Write the first letter of the word.**
- **Find the word in a** dictionary **.**

You need a dictionary.

- **Answer the question.**

Word	First letter	Question	Yes or no
gorilla	g	Is this an animal?	
picture		Do people eat this?	
rugby		Is this a tree?	
add		Is this a colour?	
sandwich		Can you eat this?	
garage		Is a horse kept in it?	
mountain		Can you do this?	
dragon		Is this a monster?	
uniform		Do people wear this?	

Now try this!

- **Choose three words from the chart.**
- **Write their** definitions **.**

1. _____

_____

2. _____

_____

3. _____

_____

Teachers' note The children should first complete the activity on page 110. Revise how to find words alphabetically in the most appropriate section of the dictionary. For lower-achieving children you could cut out the words and show them how to move the word down the pages for that letter until they find the word which matches it.

Developing Literacy
Non-fiction Compendium:
Ages 4–7
© A & C BLACK

Definitions: 1

• **Match the words to their** definitions . Use a dictionary.

Words

 jelly  owl ice

 clown astronaut 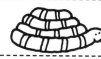 python

 tadpole elf monster

Definitions

A large frightening creature found in stories.	Frozen water.	A person who travels in space.
A young frog or toad.	A circus actor who makes people laugh.	A sweet, wobbly food.
A tiny person in fairy tales.	A bird with a flat face and large eyes. It hunts small animals at night.	A kind of snake.

 • **Put the words in alphabetical order, with their definitions.**

Teachers' note The children should first complete pages 110 and 111. As an introduction, give them some words to find in a dictionary and ask them to read out the definitions. For the extension activity, you could give the children paper on which they could glue the words and definitions: split the paper into 26 boxes and write each letter of the alphabet in a separate box.

Developing Literacy
Non-fiction Compendium:
Ages 4–7
© A & C BLACK

- **Read the** definitions **.**

- **Match them to the words.**

Use a dictionary.

- **Write the words on the crossword puzzle.**

1 b	i	2 r	t	h	3 d	a	4 y

Words

all
bird
birthday
draw
ear
kettle
key
rat
rice
rocket
tar
year
yellow

Across

1. The day you were born (8).
5. A food grain grown in hot, wet places (4).
6. Everything (3).
7. A pot with a lid and a spout, used for boiling water (6).
10. Twelve months (4).
11. A small mammal with sharp teeth and a long tail (3).

Down

1. An animal with a beak, feathers and wings (4).
2. A spacecraft with an engine (6).
3. To make a picture using a pencil (4).
4. The colour of a lemon (6).
7. A tool for opening locks (3).
8. Black sticky material used on roads (3).
9. Part of the body used for listening (3).

- **Write three words. Write their definitions.**

- **Mix them up. Ask a friend to match them.**

Teachers' note The children should first have completed the activities on pages 110–112. If necessary, explain how the answers on a crossword puzzle are numbered and point out why there is, say, no '2 Across'. Model how to find and fill in the first answer.

Developing Literacy
Non-fiction Compendium:
Ages 4–7
© A & C BLACK

- **Match the words to the joke** definitions.
- **Write the words in the joke dictionary.**

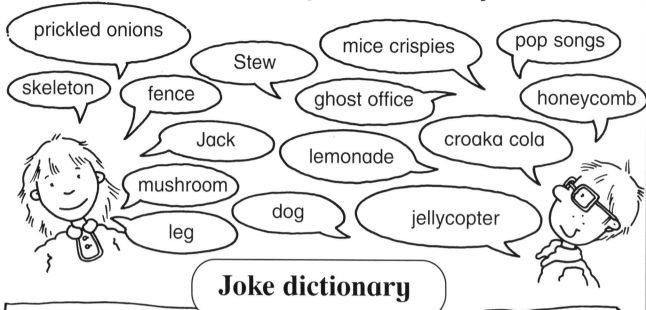

prickled onions

mice crispies

pop songs

skeleton

fence

Stew

ghost office

honeycomb

Jack

lemonade

croaka cola

mushroom

dog

jellycopter

leg

Joke dictionary

bulldozer	A sleeping bull.
	A drink for frogs.
	An animal which has a coat and pants.
	Something which can go round a field without moving.
	A place where spooks buy stamps.

Teachers' note Use this with page 115. You could introduce the activity by asking the children to give the answers to jokes: for example, 'What do you get when you cross a sheep and a kangaroo?' – 'A woolly jumper'. Model how to make definitions from the jokes (ask them for the definition of a woolly jumper: a cross between a sheep and a kangaroo). Continued on page 115.

Developing Literacy
Non-fiction Compendium:
Ages 4–7
© A & C BLACK

Joke dictionary: 2

_____ A hairdressing tool for bees.

_____ A man with a car on his head.

_____ A wobbly flying machine.

_____ Something which has a bottom at the top.

_____ First aid for lemons.

_____ A cat's breakfast.

_____ The world's smallest room.

_____ Dad's tunes.

_____ A hedgehog's favourite food.

_____ Someone who has nobody to talk to.

_____ A man with a saucepan on his head.

Now try this!

• **Write three more joke definitions.**

Teachers' note Continued from page 114. Ask the children to bring in books of jokes and examples of 'definition' jokes. They could make a class dictionary of joke definitions in a word-processed table, and then use the sorting function on the computer to arrange the definitions in alphabetical order. Encourage them to notice what happens to words beginning with the same letter.

Developing Literacy
Non-fiction Compendium:
Ages 4–7
© A & C BLACK

Bo Peep's address book

Little Bo Peep keeps losing her friends' addresses!

- **Cut out the names and addresses.**
- **Put them in** alphabetical order **of family name.**
- **Glue them into an address book.**

Jack Horner 2 Plum Lane Puddingtown 	Bobby Shaftoe The Sea House Saltsea 
Mother Hubbard The Dog House Boneville 	Miss Muffet The Tuffet Spiderly 
Humpty Dumpty The Wall Eggtown 	Incey Wincey The Spout Spiderly 
Dr Foster 1 Puddle Road Not Gloucester 	Peter Piper 3 Pickle Avenue Pepperton 
Lucy Locket 2 Lost Pocket Street Ribbon 	Jack Sprat 3 Fatfree Drive Leantown 

Teachers' note Help the children to make a simple address book, for example by folding in half two sheets of A4 paper and putting one inside the other (you could staple or glue the fold). Introduce the activity by writing on strips of paper the personal names of five children. With the class, put them in alphabetical order. Then add the family names, and discuss how to order them.

**Developing Literacy
Non-fiction Compendium:
Ages 4–7
© A & C BLACK**

Facts are true. Fiction is made up.

• Write whether each sentence is fact or fiction.

The troll was hiding under the bridge.

fiction

An acorn is the fruit of an oak tree.

Magnets can have different shapes.

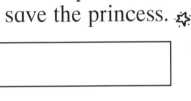

The good fairy cast a spell to save the princess.

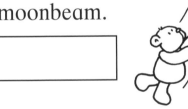

The little bear climbed up a moonbeam.

In the mud was a single huge footprint with three claws.

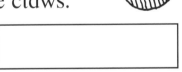

Snowflakes have six points. No two snowflakes are the same.

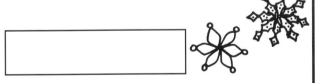

• Write two more sentences which are facts.
• Write two more sentences which are fiction.

Teachers' note Explain the terms 'fact' and 'fiction', and show the children examples of each. You could read out sentences from fiction and non-fiction books and play a game similar to 'Simon says'. The children put up their hands after a sentence which is 'fact' but not after one which is 'fiction'.

Developing Literacy
Non-fiction Compendium:
Ages 4–7
© A & C BLACK

Non-fiction features

- **Look at four different books in your classroom.**
- **Complete the chart.**

Title	Author	Words on back cover which tell you what is in the book	Is there a contents page?	Is there an index?	Is there a glossary?	Is it fiction or non-fiction?

- **Write the titles of three other** non-fiction **books.**
- **Write what each book is about.**

Teachers' note You could begin by holding up a book; ask the children to look at the front and back covers and to decide whether it is fiction or non-fiction. Draw attention to the important features of non-fiction books. For this activity, the children should work in small groups. Each group needs a selection of fiction and non-fiction books.

Developing Literacy
Non-fiction Compendium:
Ages 4–7
© A & C BLACK

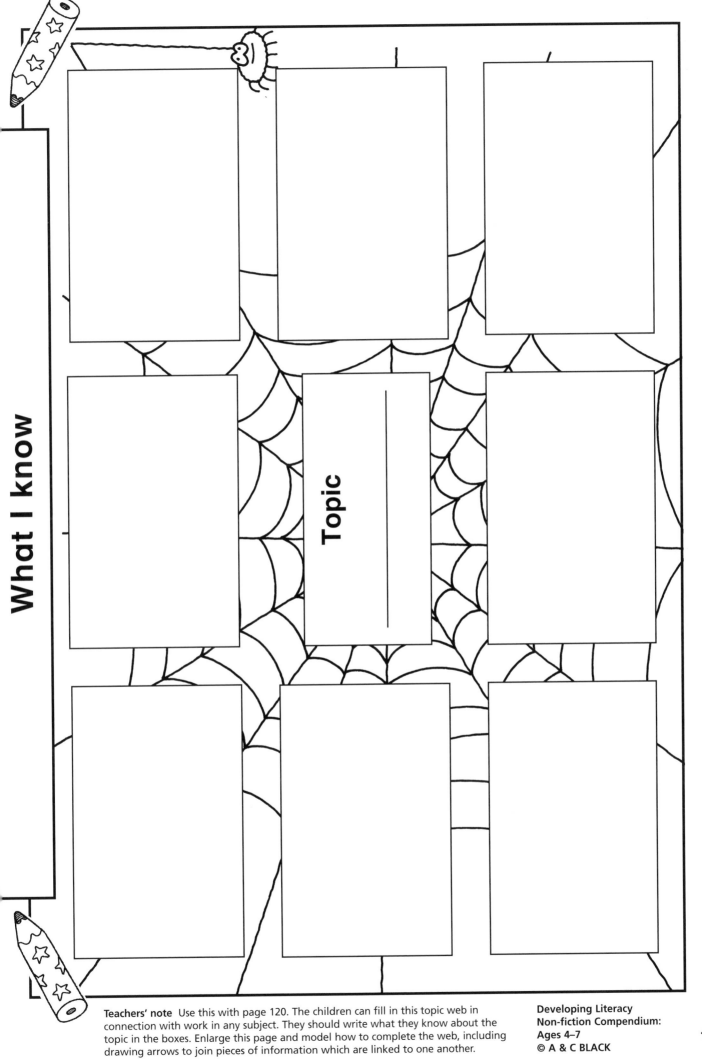

What I know

Topic _____

Teachers' note Use this with page 120. The children can fill in this topic web in connection with work in any subject. They should write what they know about the topic in the boxes. Enlarge this page and model how to complete the web, including drawing arrows to join pieces of information which are linked to one another.

Developing Literacy
Non-fiction Compendium:
Ages 4–7
© A & C BLACK

Questions and answers

Topic: _____

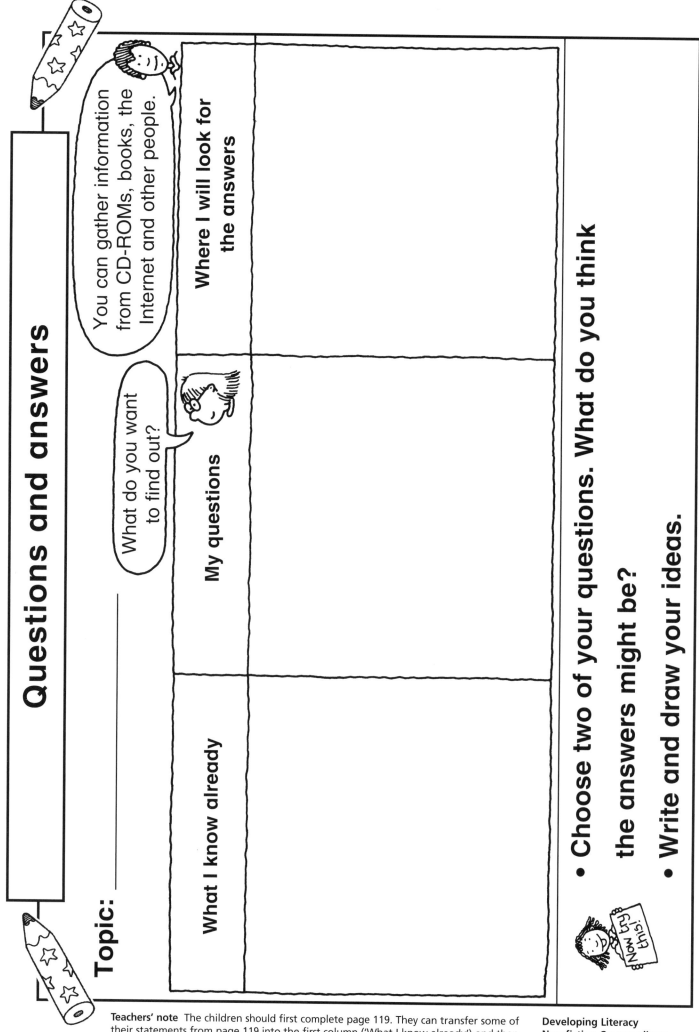

You can gather information from CD-ROMs, books, the Internet and other people.

Where I will look for the answers

What do you want to find out?

My questions

What I know already

- **Choose two of your questions. What do you think the answers might be?**
- **Write and draw your ideas.**

Now try this!

Teachers' note The children should first complete page 119. They can transfer some of their statements from page 119 into the first column ('What I know already') and then write questions to enable them to find out more, or to check if their knowledge of the topic is correct. Discuss information sources the children could use besides books.

Developing Literacy
Non-fiction Compendium:
Ages 4–7
© A & C BLACK

Skim a text

- **Read the children's questions.**

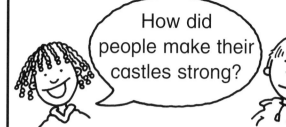

How did people make their castles strong?

What plants grow in Antarctica?

How do Hindus celebrate Divali?

- **Choose books which might help the children.**

- **Check the** | contents page | **,** | sub-headings | **,**

  | illustrations | **and** | index | **.**

- **Fill in the chart.**

Question	Title of book	Will the book help? List useful pages.
How did people make their castles strong?	_____ _____	
What plants grow in Antarctica?	_____ _____	
How do Hindus celebrate Divali?	_____ _____	

Now try this!

- **Think of a question of your own.**

- **Draw a chart like the one on this page.**

- **Fill in your chart.**

Teachers' note The children should first complete the activities on pages 119 and 120. You could begin by modelling how to find the answer to another question (for instance, 'What makes it rain?'). Show a selection of books and ask the children which ones might help and how they can tell. Model how to skim books to see if they will be useful.

**Developing Literacy
Non-fiction Compendium:
Ages 4–7
© A & C BLACK**

Find the information

Topic _____

My question _____

_____

Book title _____

_____

Look at the contents page.

Useful chapters

Chapter number	Chapter heading	Page

Useful sub-headings

Sub-heading	Page

Useful index words

Word	Pages

• **Write the answer to your question.**

Teachers' note The children should first complete the activities on pages 119–121. Choose one of the books used to introduce the previous activity and model how to skim it quickly to find the information needed. A useful way of doing this is to carry out the process while 'thinking aloud' about what you are doing.

Developing Literacy
Non-fiction Compendium:
Ages 4–7
© A & C BLACK

Text scan

- ## Read Mair and Jay's chart.

Topic Birds		
What we already know	**What we want to know**	**Where we will look to find out**
Some birds go away in the winter.	Why do the birds go away? Where do they go?	'See for yourself: Snow and Ice' by Kay Davies and Wendy Oldfield

The children think page 18 will help them.

- ## Read the text.

- ## Underline the important words.

Animals in winter

It is hard for birds to find food in winter. The blackbird in the picture is looking for food in the snow. Many of the insects and plants that birds eat die in cold weather. If ponds freeze, it is hard for birds to find water to drink.

A blackbird

Some birds fly away to warmer countries for the winter, where there are plenty of insects to eat.

You can give birds water and food. Mix nuts and seeds with fat. Put the mixture into something like this bell or half a coconut shell. Let the mixture set. Hang it up outside with a piece of string.

18

- ## Find another useful book for the children.

- ## Look for a helpful page.

- ## Write the important words from the page.

Teachers' note The children should first complete the activities on pages 119–122. Introduce the activity by reading the chart together. Ask on what topic the children in the activity are working, what they know about it, what they want to find out and where they are going to look. Encourage the children to consider how Mair and Jay knew that page 18 in their book would help them.

Developing Literacy
Non-fiction Compendium:
Ages 4–7
© A & C BLACK

123

Bring and buy sale

- **Look at the children's** plan **.**

entrance

- **Write which child sells each item.**

a tin of soup — Adam

a cherry cake — _____

a jigsaw puzzle — _____

a jumper — _____

a cactus plant — _____

a ticket for the sale — _____

a dictionary — _____

- **Write three more questions about the bring and buy sale.**
- **Give them to a friend to answer.**

Teachers' note Discuss the children's experiences of bring and buy sales; ask what people buy there and where the sale goods come from. You could encourage the children to consider what they would bring in to sell if the class were to hold a bring and buy sale. Invite them to think about how they would organise it. Discuss and write labels and signs which would be useful.

Developing Literacy
Non-fiction Compendium:
Ages 4–7
© A & C BLACK

Gran's schooldays: 1

The children asked Laura's gran about her schooldays in the 1940s.

• Read their questions and notes.

| Questions | Notes |

Did you have felt-tipped pens?

No felt-tips. No ballpoint pens.
Pen – wooden handle, metal nib.
Dipped in ink.
Ink in pot in hole in desktop.
Pencil crayons.

What subjects did you learn?

Eng. Maths. Nature study. Art.
PT (phys. training).
Girls – needlework. Boys – handicraft.

What was your uniform like?

Navy blue gymslip, cardigan, white blouse, school tie, white ankle-socks.
Black or brown lace-up shoes.
Navy blue blazer + beret.

What did the boys wear?

Grey shorts, pullover, white shirt, school tie, grey knee-socks.
Black or brown lace-up shoes.
Navy blue blazer + cap.

What did you do at lunchtime?

School dinner 6d. each (old money) – or go home. No packed lunch.
12.00–1.30.

Teachers' note Use this with page 126. The children might need to use dictionaries and information books to find the meanings of some of the words in the notes. It may be necessary to revise how to use glossaries and indexes for this.

Developing Literacy
Non-fiction Compendium:
Ages 4–7
© A & C BLACK

- **Write about Laura's gran's schooldays.**

Use the sub-headings.

Write sentences.

School in the 1940s

Writing

In the 1940s _____

_____

_____

Subjects

Girls and boys both learned _____

_____

_____

Girls' uniform

Laura's gran wore _____

_____

_____

Boys' uniform

Boys wore _____

_____

_____

Lunch

At lunchtime children _____

_____

_____

Teachers' note Use this with page 125. Draw attention to how the sub-headings have come from the questions on page 125. The children could underline the key words in those questions. In their work in history and other subjects, they could look for key words in the questions they pose, and use these words for sub-headings.

Developing Literacy Non-fiction Compendium: Ages 4–7 © A & C BLACK

Use a chart

- **List as many different types of building as you can.**

Use information books.

barn, theatre, flats, factory, _____

_____

_____

- **Write the names of the buildings on the** chart **.**

Buildings			
Homes	**Leisure**	**Storage**	**Business**
flats	theatre	barn	factory

- **Make a chart for listing different kinds of furniture. Fill it in.**

Teachers' note When the children have completed the chart, encourage them to think of ways it could help them to plan a report about buildings. Ask them to suggest what sub-headings they could use in the report.

Developing Literacy
Non-fiction Compendium:
Ages 4–7
© A & C BLACK

Write a report

• **Help Daniel to improve his report.**

I saw some trees in the park. I saw some ducks on the pond.
I saw an oak tree. I saw a frog by the pond. I saw swings in
the playground in the park. I saw a dragonfly by the pond. I
saw a see-saw in the playground. I saw a willow tree and a
beech tree in the park. I saw climbing frames in the playground.

• **Use the plan to help you to re-write the report.**

Heading _____

Sub-heading _____

I saw _____.

There was an _____, a _____

and a _____.

Sub-heading _____

I saw some animals by the _____.

There was a _____,

a _____ and some _____.

Sub-heading _____

In the playground I saw _____,

a _____ and _____.

What is
the report
about?

Now try this!

• **Think of useful words for starting**

sentences in a report. Make a list.

Examples: | There is | | There are | | I saw |

Teachers' note Read the report with the children. Ask them what it is about and what heading they could give it. Point out that it is rather mixed up, because the writer has not grouped the different kinds of things he saw. Ask the children to look for groups of things, such as trees.

Developing Literacy
Non-fiction Compendium:
Ages 4–7
© A & C BLACK